GCSE /Y9 SCIENCE
MASTERY
PRACTICE BOOK

Get the highest grades

Created by: Dr Tony Sherborne

Lead writer: Gemma Young

Teacher writers: Robin Young, Ruth Smith, Kat Day, Frances Rattigan, Alison Dennis

Design by: Alexandra Okada

mastery science

Contents

How to use the book

Applying what you know is not easy. Keep trying, and learn from your mistakes. With practice you will master the concepts and be confident with whatever examiners ask.

The *Example* pages have 3 steps:

- ✓ Diagram
- ✓ Values
- ✓ Unknown
- ✓ Concept

1. Detect. Work out what you need to do to answer the question. There are 4 different parts to detect:
- diagram, makes the situation clearer
- values, information that the question provides
- unknown, what you have to find out
- concept, the key idea that the question is applying

2. Recall. Bring to mind what you already know about the concept. Showing it visually helps the thinking process.

3. Solve. Go from what you know to the answer, step-by-step. When Solve involves an explanation, it is set out as a scientific argument:
- claim, the answer that you believe it true
- evidence, information in the question or knowledge
- reasoning, how to get from the evidence to the answer

Why is this evidence?

Do answer the questions in speech bubbles. This will help you follow the example and remember the main points.

Your turn

The *Your Turn* pages have three practice questions. The first is very similar to the example. Look back and copy the steps. The other two questions might look different but they are testing the same thinking process.

Use the scoring box to check how you're doing. Award yourself 3 points if you did Detect, Recall and Solve well. Subtract 1 point for each step you didn't do well.

Hints & Answers

If you're stuck, go to the *Hints* pages at the back. The hint is a clue or question to get you moving.

The *Answers* are online. Go to masteryscience.com. If you made a mistake, look back at the example to figure out what you did wrong.

Good luck!

1.1 Distance travelled

A jet is travelling at 67 m/s when it lands on an aircraft carrier.

The runway is 96 m and the jet comes to a stop in 2.4 seconds.
How far from the end of the runway does it stop?

 Detect

☑ Concept — The description involves changing speed, so the concept is acceleration.

☑ Diagram

☑ Values

as the jet stops, final speed, v = 0 m/s | 96 m | initial speed, u = 67 m/s

x

the jet is decelerating.
The time to decelerate, t = 2.4 s

☑ Unknown — I need to find the distance, x, from where the jet stops to the end of the runway.

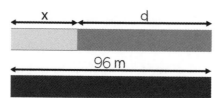

x   d

96 m

I cannot calculate x directly as the distance travelled is d.

So first I calculate d, using a graph or a formula.
Then I can work out x, because x = 96-d.

Recall

Method 1. Area under a speed/time graph

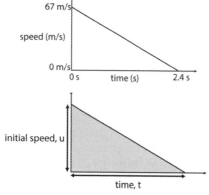

67 m/s
speed (m/s)
0 m/s
0 s   time (s)   2.4 s

Here is the speed / time graph for the jet's motion.

initial speed, u
time, t

The distance travelled in time t = the area under the graph.
As the area is a triangle,
distance travelled = ½ × base × height
$\qquad$ = ½ × initial speed × time
$\qquad$ = ½ × u × t

Recall

Method 2. Distance-speed-time formula

Distance travelled is related to speed by this formula:

distance = average speed × time

I can calculate this   I know t = 2.4 s

$$\text{average speed} = \frac{\text{initial speed} + \text{final speed}}{2}$$

I know u = 67 m/s   I know v = 0

As we know all the quantities, we can calculate distance from the formula.

> Why is this the average speed?

 Solve

Method 1. Area under a speed/time graph

Here is a speed-time graph of the jet's motion.

First find d, the distance the jet travels.

d = area of the triangle
= ½ × speed × time
= 0.5 × 67 × 2.4
= 80.4 m

Then find **x**, the distance to the end of the runway.
We know the runway = 96 m.
x = 96 m - d
= 96 – 80.4
= 15.6 m

> How do you calculate the area under the graph?

Method 2. Distance-speed-time formula
First, calculate average speed:

$$\text{average speed} = \frac{\text{initial speed} + \text{final speed}}{2}$$
= (67+0)/2
= 33.5 m/s

Then, calculate distance travelled, d:
d = average speed × time
= 33.5 × 2.4
= 80.4 m

We know the runway = 96 m.
The distance, **x**, to the end of the runway = 96 m - d. So x = 96 – 80.4 = 15.6 m

Hint p.121

Your turn

1

A driver travels at 28 m/s and notices a sheep in the road. The driver brakes when the sheep is 125 m away. The car stops in 8.5 s.
How far from the sheep is the car when it stops?

2

A rocket going to a space station is fired vertically into space. It reaches a speed of 0.75 km/s in 2 minutes.
How far has it travelled in this time?
(Assume its acceleration is constant).

3

35 m/s   25 m/s

gap

A stunt rider goes up a ramp and jumps over a gap. On take-off, her horizontal speed is 35 m/s. On landing, her horizontal speed is 25 m/s. She is in the air for 1.5 seconds.
a) Sketch a speed-time graph of the motion across the gap.
b) Calculate the length of the gap.

4

A car stopped at the traffic lights. It then accelerated to a top speed of 35 m/s while travelling 350 m.

How long did this take?

1   /3   **2**   /3   **3**   /3   **4**   /3   Total   /12   © Mastery Science 2018

1.2 Acceleration and gradients

The statements describe the motion of a bicycle during a ride.

A Acceleration from 0 to 11 m/s in 40 seconds

B Constant velocity for 20 seconds

C Climbing a hill for 1 minute, slowing to 6.0 m/s at the top

D Descending for 40 seconds, increasing to 14 m/s at the bottom

E Applying the brakes and stopping in 20 seconds

a) Sketch a graph of the motion and explain which stage of the ride have the maximum and minimum acceleration

b) Calculate the maximum acceleration and maximum deceleration.

 Detect

✓ **Concept**

✓ **Diagram**

The question is about finding acceleration from graphs and an equation.

Stage of journey	A start	B constant velocity	C hill climb	D downhill	E braking
Velocity in m/s	0 - 11	11	11 - 6	6 - 14	14 - 0
Length of time in s	40	20	60	40	20

✓ **Values**

✓ **Unknown**

I need to compare the accelerations and I need a formula to calculate acceleration.

 Recall

1. How the gradient of a velocity-time graph tells you the acceleration.

The gradient of a velocity -time graph means acceleration. Why?

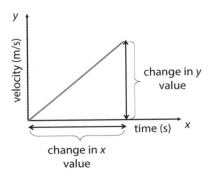

The definition of acceleration is:

$$\text{acceleration (m/s}^2) = \frac{\text{change in velocity (m/s)}}{\text{time taken (s)}}$$

final - initial velocity

When an object slows down the change in velocity is negative - this is deceleration.

Velocity and speed both tell you how fast an object travels. Velocity also tells you the direction: a negative value means moving in the opposite direction.

The definition of a gradient is:

$$\text{gradient} = \frac{\text{change in y value}}{\text{change in x value}}$$

change in velocity

time taken

Therefore gradient means acceleration.

Recall

A steeper line means a bigger gradient. Bigger positive gradient means bigger acceleration.

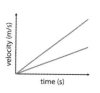

A steeper line down-wards means a bigger deceleration.

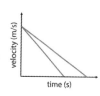

How do I know which is the steepest gradient?

2. How negative velocity shows movement in opposite direction.

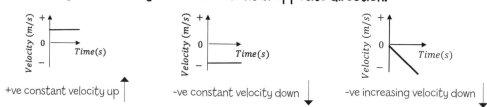

+ve constant velocity up ↑

-ve constant velocity down ↓

-ve increasing velocity down ↓

Solve

a) Sketch a velocity time graph.

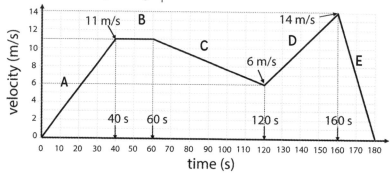

Maximum acceleration: stage A.

This is the steepest part of the line going upwards.

The gradient represents the acceleration and A has the biggest positive gradient.

✓ Claim
✓ Evidence
✓ Reasoning

Maximum deceleration: stage E.

This is the steepest part of the line going downwards.

The maximum deceleration is when the negative gradient is biggest.

✓ Claim
✓ Evidence
✓ Reasoning

b) Use a formula to calculate acceleration.

Stage A

Acceleration = gradient = $\dfrac{\text{change in velocity}}{\text{time taken}}$

$$= \frac{11 - 0}{40} = 0.275 \text{ m/s}^2$$

Stage E

Deceleration = gradient = $\dfrac{\text{change in velocity}}{\text{time taken}}$

$$= \frac{14 - 0}{20} = 0.7 \text{ m/s}^2$$

This is a negative acceleration.

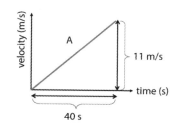

1

A train leaves the station and reaches 22.2 m/s after 600 seconds. It continues at this speed for 900 seconds. Then it accelerates to 50 m/s over the next 300 seconds.

a) Sketch a speed time graph of the journey and calculate the acceleration at each stage.

b) During which part of the ride will passengers notice their speed changing fastest?

2

In a theme park ride, the elevator goes from stationary to a top speed of 17.5 m/s while dropping 40 m in 1.5 s.

a) Calculate the acceleration.

b) Sketch a velocity time graph for the elevator ride.

3 A ball is thrown vertically upwards and then caught again

a) Which graph best shows how its velocity changes? Explain your choice.

b) For the graph you chose, calculate the acceleration during the first 1.5 seconds.

A

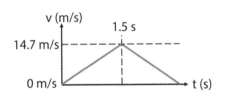

B

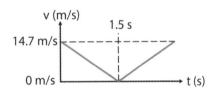

C

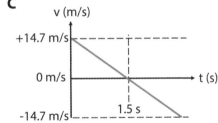

D

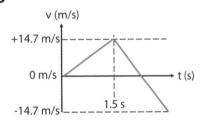

4

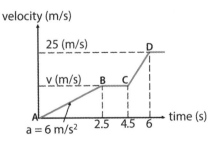

The graph shows a motorcyclist's journey.

From A to B she accelerates at 6 m/s² for 2.5 s to velocity v.

From B to C she cruises at constant velocity for 2 s.

From C to D she accelerates for 1.5 s to a top speed (velocity) of 25 m/s.

a) Calculate velocity, v.

b) Calculate her acceleration from C to D.

1.3 Equations of motion

A speeding car overtakes a police van that is travelling at 10 m/s. The police give chase and accelerate at 3 m/s² for a quarter of a kilometre. What is the final speed of the police van?

 Detect

✓ Diagram

✓ Values

✓ Unknown

✓ Concept

Distance (displacement)	Initial speed (velocity)	Final speed (velocity)	Acceleration	Time
s	u	v	a	t
✓	✓	?	✓	✗
250 m	10 m/s	?	3 m/s²	✗

I need to convert distance to metres ¼ km = 250 m

I need to find out final speed, v

I don't know time, t

This question is about acceleration and using an equation of motion.

 Recall

> Which values do I know, which are to find out?

How to find the right equation of motion to use

I need an equation that includes the values and only one unknown.

Which equation?	s	u	v	a	t
$a = \dfrac{\Delta v}{t} = \dfrac{v - u}{t}$	✗	✓	✓	✓	✓
$s = v \times t$	✓	✗	✓	✗	✓
$v^2 - u^2 = 2as$	✓	✓	✓	✓	✗

this is the only equation without time, t

I need to use this one   I know s, u and a. I want to find v. So I need to rearrange the equation.

Method 1. Rearrange the equation first then substitute values.

Make v the subject

to get v² on its own, add u²

$$v^2 - u^2 = 2as$$
$$+ u^2 \qquad + u^2$$

➡ $v^2 = u^2 + 2as$

to change v² to v, take square root

$$v^2 = u^2 + 2as$$
$$\sqrt{} \qquad \sqrt{}$$

➡ $v = \sqrt{u^2 + 2as}$

Make u the subject

to get u² on its own, subtract 2as

$$v^2 = u^2 + 2as$$
$$-2as \qquad -2as$$

➡ $v^2 - 2as = u^2$

to change u² to u, take the square root

$$u^2 = v^2 - 2as$$
$$\sqrt{} \qquad \sqrt{}$$

➡ $u = \sqrt{v^2 - 2as}$

Make a the subject

To get a on its own, divide by 2s

$v^2 - u^2 = 2as$

$\div 2s \quad \div 2s$

$\dfrac{v^2 - u^2}{2s} = a$

Make s the subject

To get s on its own, divide by 2a

$v^2 - u^2 = 2as$

$\div 2a \quad \div 2a$

$\dfrac{v^2 - u^2}{2a} = s$

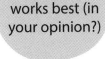

Which method works best (in your opinion?)

Method 2. Substitute values first then rearrange the equation.

$v^2 = 10^2 + (2 \times 3.0 \times 250)$ I can also solve an equation by substituting in the numbers and then solving for the unknown.

If the object is decelerating, the acceleration is a negative number.

-Ö- **Solve**

Method 1. Rearrange the equation first then substitutwe values.

The question gives values for s, u and a. I need to find v, so I use: $v^2 - u^2 = 2as$.

First make v^2 the subject $v^2 = u^2 + 2as$

Substitute in the known values $v^2 = 10^2 + (2 \times 3.0 \times 250)$

Simplify and find the value of v^2 $v^2 = 100 + 1500$

                                                     $v^2 = 1600$

To change v^2 to v, take the square root of both sides

$v^2 = 1600$

$\sqrt{} \qquad \sqrt{}$

$v^2 = \sqrt{1600} = 40 \text{ m/s}$

Method 2. Substitute values first then rearrange the equation.

Write down the equation $v^2 - u^2 = 2as$

Substitute in the known values $v^2 - 10^2 = 2 \times 3.0 \times 250$

Simplify the numbers $v^2 - 100 = 1500$

To get v^2 on its own, add 100 to both sides

$v^2 - 100 = 1500$

$+100 \qquad +100$

$v^2 = 1500 + 100$
$v^2 = 1600$

To change v^2 to v, take the square root of both sides

$v^2 = 1600$

$\sqrt{} \qquad \sqrt{}$

$v^2 = \sqrt{1600} = 40 \text{ m/s}$

1

A kingfisher dives from 6 m above a river to catch a fish. Its acceleration is 9.8 m/s².

At what speed does it hit the water?

2

275 m
Reduce speed

A car travels at 31 m/s along a motorway. The driver sees a sign to reduce his speed to 22 m/s in the next 275 m.

What is the deceleration needed to reach the new speed limit?

3

speed	braking distance
20 mph (9 m/s)	6 m
30 mph (13m/s)	14 m
40 mph (18m/s)	24 m

The diagram shows braking distances for a typical car at different speeds.

Compare the deceleration required to stop the car at both 20 mph and 40 mph.

4

a) An 800 m Olympic runner completes a 400 m lap in 50 s. What is his average speed for the lap?

b) If he accelerates from this speed by 0.15 m/s² for the last 15 m, what is his final speed?

1 /3   **2** /3   **3** /3   **4** /3   **Total** /12

 **Example**

1.4 Newton's 1st law

A man moves upwards in a lift at constant speed.

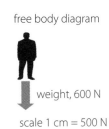

free body diagram

weight, 600 N

scale 1 cm = 500 N

a) Complete the free body diagram to show the forces on the man. Show the forces to scale.

b) Explain how the forces on the man change, and what the man will feel, if the lift is:
i) not moving, ii) moving upwards and speeding up, iii) moving upwards and slowing down.

Detect

✓ Values

✓ Unknown

✓ Concept

I know the weight and which scale to use to show the forces.
I need to identify all the other forces, and show them to scale. I also need to work out how the forces change when the lift direction or speed changes. This question is about balanced and unbalanced forces and Newton's 1st law.

Recall

1. How to draw a free body diagram.
- Show the forces acting on one object at a time.
- Use arrows of the correct length and pointing in the correct direction.
- Use the given scale.

> How do I use a force diagram to find the resultant?

2. How to combine forces.

Forces pointing in the same direction add

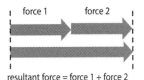

force 1   force 2

resultant force = force 1 + force 2

Forces pointing in opposite directions subtract

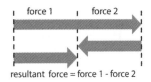

force 1   force 2

resultant force = force 1 - force 2

3. How to explain and predict motion.
Newton's 1st Law can explain motion:

If an object is stationary or moving at constant speed in the same direction, the resultant force must be 0. If the resultant is 0, the object continues at the same speed in the same direction, or remains stationary.

If the object's speed is changing, there must be a resultant force. If the resultant force is in the direction of motion, the object will speed up (accelerate).

If the resultant force is in the opposite direction to the motion, the object will slow down (decelerate).

◄———— direction of travel

constant speed or stationary
forward force
backward force
resultant force is zero

speeding up
forward force
backward force
resultant force

slowing down
forward force
backward force
resultant force

4. How your feeling of weight depends on the normal force.

You feel your weight on your feet because the normal force is pushing up on you from the floor.

When you are stationary this force is the same as your weight, because the two forces are balanced.

To make you accelerate upwards, the normal force must be greater than your weight. So you feel heavier.

When you accelerate downwards, the normal force must be less than your weight. So you feel lighter.

 Solve

I need to add a normal force from the floor pushing up. The forces are balanced, so the arrow should be the same length as the weight.

a)

scale
1 cm = 500 N

normal force
(of the lift floor on the man)

weight of the man

The magnitude of each force is
1.2 × 500 N = 600 N

How does the feeling of weight change if forces aren't balanced?

b) **i) Not moving**

normal force

weight

Weight and normal force are equal and opposite.
Resultant force = 0

The man will feel the floor of the lift is pushing on him with the same force as his weight.

direction of travel

ii) Speeding up

normal force

weight

The lift is speeding up so there must be a resultant force acting upwards. The normal force must be larger than the weight.

He feels heavier than usual because the normal force from the floor pushes up with a greater force than his weight.

iii) Slowing down

normal force

weight

The lift is slowing down so there must be a resultant force acting downwards. The weight must be larger than the normal force.

The man feels lighter because the normal force from the floor pushes up with a smaller force than his weight.

1

A skydiver has a weight of 800 N and falls at a constant speed (terminal velocity).

a) Complete the free body diagram to show the vertical forces acting on her. Show the forces to scale using 1 cm : 400 N.

b) Explain how the resultant force changes:

i) immediately her parachute opens and she slows down

ii) when she stops slowing down and reaches her final terminal velocity.

2

A car tows a caravan at constant speed along the motorway.

a) Sketch a free body diagram to show the horizontal forces acting on the car.

b) The tow bar breaks and the two vehicles separate. Predict how the motion of the car changes.

3

Sketch a set of free body diagrams to show the vertical and horizontal forces acting on a speed boat when it is:

a) still in the water   **b)** speeding up

c) moving at constant speed   **d)** slowing down

4

A kestrel of weight 1.8 N hovers in position above the ground. It flies into a wind of force 0.9 N using an equal and opposite force from its wings.

a) Draw a scale free body diagram to show the horizontal and vertical forces acting on the hovering kestrel. Choose a suitable scale.

b) When the kestrel sees its prey, it folds its wings back and makes a vertical dive.

Predict how the kestrel's motion changes at the moment it starts to dive.

1.5 Adding vectors

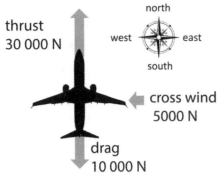

thrust
30 000 N

cross wind
5000 N

drag
10 000 N

The diagram shows a jet aircraft from above. It is flying due north with a thrust of 30 000 N. A drag force of 10 000 N acts due south.

A side wind starts blowing at 90° to the jet. Use a scale vector diagram to determine what happens to:

a) the magnitude of force on the jet.

b) the direction the jet travels in.

🔍 Detect

✓ Diagram

✓ Values

✓ Unknown

✓ Concept/skill

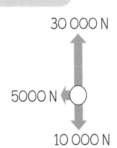

30 000 N

5000 N

10 000 N

I know the size (magnitude) and direction of the three forces acting on the jet. Two forces are parallel but acting in opposite directions and one force is acting at 90°.

I need to add these forces together to find out what the combined size (magnitude) and direction of the three forces is.

The question is asking me to find the net (resultant) force using the skill of drawing a scale vector diagram.

⚙️ Recall

1. How to add forces in parallel.

Add or subtract to find the combined effect.

Two parallel forces in the same direction add.

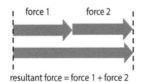

force 1   force 2

resultant force = force 1 + force 2

Two parallel forces in opposite directions subtract.

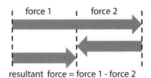

force 1   force 2

resultant force = force 1 - force 2

> How do I accurately measure arrow length?

force 2

force 1

2. How to add forces at right angles.

Use a vector diagram to find the combined effect.

Step 1. Use a ruler to draw the first force vector to scale, and in the correct direction.

force 1

cm 1 2 3 4

Choose an easy to use scale e.g. 1 cm : 1 N, 1 cm : 10 N, or 1 cm : 50 N etc. Make the arrows long enough to measure accurately and short enough to fit on the grid. Measure all lengths to the nearest mm.

Step 2. Use a ruler to draw the second force vector to scale in the correct direction.

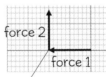

force 2

force 1

Force 2 is at 90 °. The tail of the second arrow must touch the head of the first arrow

Step 3. Draw an arrow from the start of the first vector arrow to the end of the second.

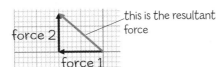

this is the resultant force

Step 4. use the ruler to measure the length of the resultant force.

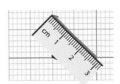

This will give the magnitude of the force vector, using your scale to convert back from cm to Newtons.

Step 5. Use a protractor to measure the direction of the force vector.

How accurately can I measure the angle on my diagram?

If the vector arrow is too small, draw a construction line along the length of the arrow to read off the angle correctly with the protractor.
Measure all angles to the nearest 1°.

 Solve

a) Before the wind blows, two forces, thrust and drag, act on the jet, but in opposite directions. We can replace these forces with a net thrust north of 30 000 - 10 000 = 20 000 N.

drag = 10 000 N, south

thrust = 30 000 N, north

thrust - drag = 20 000 N, north

20 000 N

5000 N

When the cross wind blows this adds a force west of 5000 N.

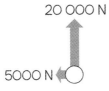

1 cm (5 000 N)

direction plane travels

4 cm (20 000 N)

θ

b) Here is a scale drawing to find the resultant force. The resultant force arrow measures 4.1 cm.

The magnitude of the force is
4.1 × 5000 = 20 500 N

So the side wind increases the magnitude of the net force.

The plane changes direction by the angle θ. I measured it with a protractor to be 14°.

So the direction changes by 14° northwest.

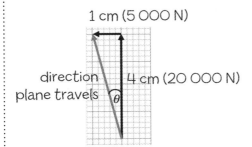

1

upthrust
0.85 N

current
0.60 N

weight
1.45 N

A stone of weight 1.45 N is dropped into a river. The upthrust is 0.85 N and the current pushes the stone sideways with a force of 0.6 N. Draw a scale vector diagram to show the direction and magnitude of the resultant force acting on the stone.

2

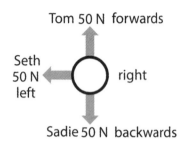

Tom 50 N forwards

Seth
50 N
left

right

Sadie 50 N backwards

Three kids tug on a hoop with the same force but in three different directions.
a) What is the magnitude and direction of the resultant force?
b) Tom lets go. Use a scale vector diagram to show how the magnitude and direction of the resultant force on the hoop changes.

3

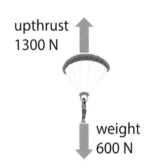

upthrust
1300 N

weight
600 N

The diagram shows the forces on a parachutist after she opens her chute.
a) What is the resultant force acting on the parachutist?
b) Draw a vector diagram to show the resultant force and direction, if a wind blows horizontally to the right with a force of 150 N.

4

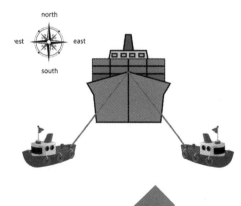

north

'est   east

south

2000 N

2000 N

Two tug boats pull a ship into the harbour. They exert an equal force of 2000 N at an angle of 90° to each other.

a) Draw a scale vector diagram 1 cm : 500 N to find the resultant force of the tug boats acting on the ship and the direction the ship is moving.

b) The left boat has engine trouble and pulls with half the force of the other boat. Draw another diagram, scale 1 cm : 500 N, to show the the resultant force on the ship and the new direction.

Student Workbook
not to be
photocopied

1 /3   **2** /3   **3** /3   **4** /3   Total   /12   © Mastery Science 2018

1.6 Vector components

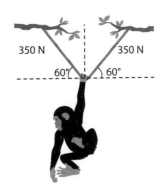

350 N   350 N

60°   60°

A chimpanzee hangs from a rope in a tree without moving. The diagram shows the size and direction of the tension forces in the rope.

a) Draw a scale vector diagram to find the vertical components of the forces in the rope.

b) Calculate the weight of the chimpanzee.

 Detect

✓ Diagram

✓ Values

✓ Unknown

✓ Concept

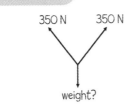

350 N   350 N

weight?

There are two tension forces in the rope pulling up the chimpanzee. Its weight is pulling down.
The forces in the rope are given.
a) I first need to find the component of each of the forces that are acting vertically upwards.
b) I then need to find the weight pulling down.

The question is about forces: balanced & unbalanced, and vector components. I need to use the skill of scale drawing.

 Recall

1. How to split a force into its components.

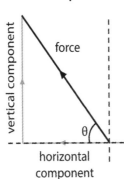

vertical component

force

θ

horizontal component

If a force acts at angle θ:
- the horizontal component is the amount of force that acts horizontally.
- the vertical component is the amount of the force that act vertically.

The forces make up a right angled triangle:
- the overall force is the hypotenuse
- the horizontal component is the base
- the vertical component is the height

2. How the forces on a stationery object must be balanced.

Both horizontal and vertical forces on an object in equilibrium must be balanced.

Horizontal forces

| tension | tension |

The horizontal components of the tension act to the left and right. They are equal and opposite and cancel out.

Vertical forces

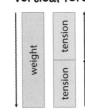

weight | tension / tension

The chimp's weight acts downwards. The components of the tension act upwards. These forces must balance:

↓ weight = ↑ sum of the two vertical components

3. How to find the components of a force using a vector diagram.

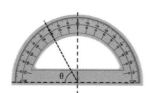

Step 1. Use a protractor and a ruler to draw construction lines at the correct angle θ to the horizontal.

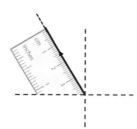

Step 2. Draw the force arrow to the correct scale length using a ruler.

Choose an easy to use scale e.g. 1 cm : 1 N, 1 cm : 10 N, or 1 cm : 50 N etc.
Make sure the arrows are long enough to measure accurately but short enough to fit on the grid.

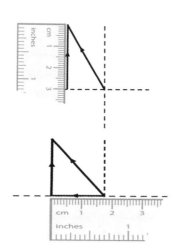

Step 3. . Find the size (magnitude) of the vertical component of each force by drawing a vertical arrow for each force and measuring its length with a ruler.

Do the same for the horizontal component.

 Solve

a) Here is a scale drawing to find the vertical component of each tension. I don't need to find the horizontal components.

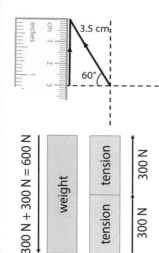

The scale is 1 cm : 100 N
The vertical component is 3.0 cm.
This represents a force of 300 N upwards.

b) The total amount of force acting vertically upwards is:
300 + 300 = 600 N

The forces on the chimpanzee are balanced.
So the weight of the chimpanzee must be 600 N acting downward.

Your turn

1

500N   500N
30°   30°

A girl is walking a tightrope. The diagram shows the size and direction of the two tension forces in the rope.
a) Draw a scale vector diagram to find the vertical components of the two forces in the rope.
b) Calculate the weight of the girl.

2

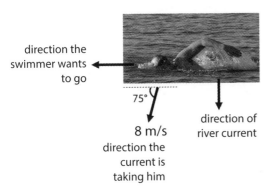

Dad pulls his son along the snow on a sledge. The rope is at an angle of 45° to the horizontal. The tension in the rope is 450 N.
a) Use a scale vector diagram to find how much of the force acts horizontally to pull the sledge.
b) Explain why he would find it easier to pull the sledge at an angle of 30°.

3

direction the
swimmer wants
to go

75°

8 m/s
direction the
current is
taking him

direction of
river current

A swimmer is trying to swim across a river, but the current is pulling him along in the wrong direction.
a) Use a scale vector diagram to find how fast the swimmer is moving in the direction he wants to go in and how fast the river current is.
b) If the river current was half the speed, how would this effect his speed and direction of travel?

4

horizontal
component   vertical
component
= 500 kN

upthrust   30°

30°

weight = 500 kN

When the pilot of a plane wants to turn, she dips the wing down by 30°. The plane flies horizontally, supported by an upthrust from the air under the wings.
a) Explain why the vertical component of the upthrust needs to be 500 kN to keep the plane flying horizontally.
b) Use a scale drawing to work out the magnitude of the upthrust.

1	/3	**2**	/3	**3**	/3	**4**	/3	Total	/12

 **Example**

2.1 Thermal transfer By particles

Rich Victorians built ice houses underground to store ice blocks from frozen lakes.
In the summer, their kitchens had a ready supply of ice.
Explain how the ice house keeps ice frozen even in the summer time.

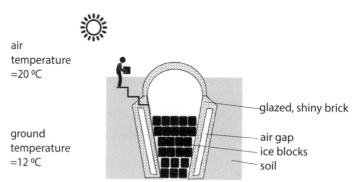

air temperature =20 ºC

ground temperature =12 ºC

glazed, shiny brick
air gap
ice blocks
soil

 Detect

☑ Values

I know the ice remains below 0 °C. Between the ice and the warm air are layers of brick, an air gap and the soil.

☑ Unknown

I need to explain why the warmer ground, air temperature and the sun's rays do not heat the ice above 0 °C.

☑ Concept

This question is about the different ways that thermal transfer of energy takes place and how to limit it.

 Recall

1. How radiation is absorbed or reflected from surfaces.

All objects emit radiation. Surfaces absorb, transmit and reflect it. The amount depends on the type of surface.

Matt and dark surfaces are good absorbers of radiation and reflect less. They also emit more heat. So dark surfaces heat up and cool down quickly.

White or shiny surfaces are good reflectors and poor absorbers of radiation. This means that they don't heat up or cool down easily.

2. How energy moves through materials by conduction.

On the warm side:
particles vibrate more and pass on their movement when they collide with neighbouring particles. This is called conduction.

solid

energy

On the cold side:
soon the collisions transfer energy to the particles on this side. Therefore, it warms up.

Do we want to keep heat in or out?

22

What sequence of layers does the energy travel through?

 Recall

3. How the rate of conduction depends on the state of matter.

Particles in a gas are much more spread out. They don't collide as often as they do in a solid. So in air, it takes longer to transfer energy from the warmer to the cooler side.
Air has a low thermal conductivity.

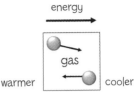

3. How the rate of conduction depends on thickness.

It takes longer for the energy to pass through a thicker layer because there are more particles to move along.
Energy also spreads out and dissipates in a thicker layer because there is more material. Therefore, less energy passes all the way through.

 Solve

✓ **Claim**

The ice stays frozen because the the ice house is designed to decrease the rate of energy transfer by reflection, and by decreasing conduction.

✓ **Evidence**
✓ **Reasoning**

Reflection
The roof is made from shiny bricks, so most of the sun's radiation is reflected.

✓ **Evidence**

✓ **Reasoning**

Conduction
There is a thick layer of soil between the ice house and the outside air.
Thermal conduction through the soil and brick is slower, and the energy gets spread out through the ground instead of all going into the brick.

the sun's intense radiation hits the bricks

Air gap
✓ **Evidence**
✓ **Reasoning**

In air, particles are spread far apart.
Gas has low thermal conductivity and dramatically slows the rate of energy reaching the ice.

The combination of these features makes the rate of energy transfer to the ice very slow. The ice does not receive enough energy to melt.

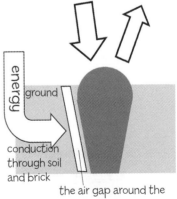

the air gap around the ice house is a gas

Hint p.121

Your turn

1

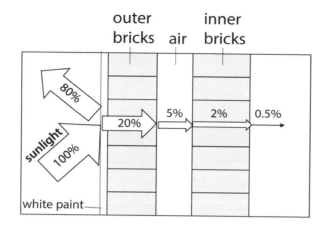

outer bricks | air | inner bricks

A cavity wall is made of two layers of bricks with an air gap in between. It is painted white on the outside.

Explain why only a small fraction of the sun's energy reaches the inside of the house.

2 A wetsuit company advert says: "Our thick, 6 mm wetsuit keeps you comfortable in a wider range of water temperatures than a thin, 3 mm wetsuit".

a) Explain how the thick wetsuit keeps your skin at a more comfortable temperature when the water is cold.

b) Explain why a swimmer might prefer the thin wetsuit in warmer water.

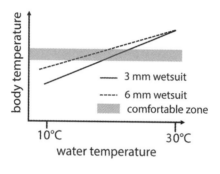

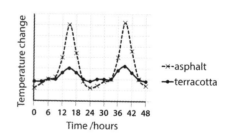

Wetsuits are made from a closed cell foam, which has many bubbles of nitrogen gas trapped inside.

3 On a farm, the roofs of the animal sheds are made out of either asphalt or terracotta. Use the information about the materials to explain the differences in daily temperatures for each roof.

Asphalt roof: matt black, 1 mm thick

Terracotta: glazed, shiny, 5 mm thick

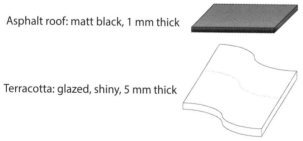

4

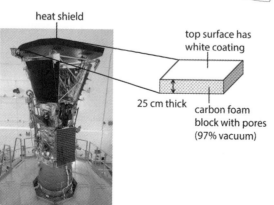

heat shield

top surface has white coating

25 cm thick

carbon foam block with pores (97% vacuum)

The Parker Solar Probe will travel closer to the Sun than any other craft has. Explain how the design of its heat shield keeps the scientific instruments cool.

Student Workbook not to be photocopied

| **1** /3 | **2** /3 | **3** /3 | **4** /3 | Total /12 | © Mastery Science 2018

2.2 Thermal transfer rates

Stan wanted to find out if cola cools quicker in a metal can or plastic bottle. He put both in a cooler bag chilled to a temperature of 0 °C and measured how the temperature changed with time.

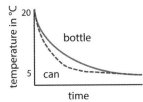

a) Explain the shapes of the lines on the graph.
b) Sketch a temperature-time graph for the air in the cooler bag.

 Detect

✓ **Values**

✓ **Unknown**

✓ **Concept**

a) The question tells me both liquids cool from 20 - 5 °C and that they are surrounded by colder air at 0 °C.
I need to explain why the cooling curve for the can is steeper than that of the bottle. Also, why both curves cool down to the same final temperature.
b) To sketch the graph, I need to work out the final temperature of the air, and how the temperature, including the steepness of the line, varies with time.
This question is about what affects the rate of thermal (energy) transfer.

 Recall

1. How a temperature difference between objects leads to energy transfer.

cools
from 20 °C

energy

warms up
from 0 °C

Energy moves from the can to the bag until both reach the same temperature.

2. How the steepness of the graph shows the rate of energy transfer.

The steepness of the graph is called the gradient.

$$\text{gradient} = \frac{(\text{change in y value})}{(\text{change in x value})} = \frac{\text{change in temperature}}{\text{change in time}}$$

change in
y value

change in x value

So the steepness means the rate of change of temperature with time.
A temperature change means energy is transferred.
So the gradient also shows the rate of energy transfer.

a ratio with time in the denominator is called a rate

To find the gradient at a point on a curve, draw a tangent line, touching the curve at that point. Find the gradient of the tangent.

steep gradient = fast rate of energy transfer (temperature changes fast)

shallow gradient = slow rate of energy transfer (temperature changes slowly)

3. How the type of material affects energy transfer.

Energy passes slowly along the glass particles. Glass has a low thermal conductivity.

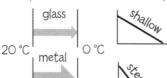

The rate of energy transfer is slow so temperature changes slowly.

The rate of energy transfer is fast so temperature changes quickly.

Energy passes quickly along the metal particles. Metal has a high thermal conductivity.

4. How the thickness of material affects energy transfer.

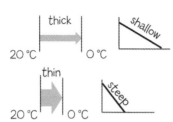

In a thick material, there are more particles to pass along. The rate of energy transfer is slower.

In a thin material, there are fewer particles to pass along. The rate of energy transfer is fast.

5. How temperature difference affects energy transfer.

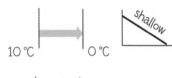

When the temperature difference is smaller, the rate of energy transfer is slower.

When the temperature difference is bigger, the rate of energy transfer is faster.

> How does this explain the curved graph in the question?

 Solve

✓ **Claim**

a) The can's cooling curve is initially steeper than the bottle's because it allows a faster rate of energy transfer.

✓ **Evidence**

The metal can has a higher thermal conductivity than glass. It is three times thinner than the glass.

✓ **Reasoning**

Both of these factors make the rate of energy transfer faster across the metal. This means the temperature drops faster.

✓ **Claim**
✓ **Evidence**

The gradient is steepest at the very start, when energy transfer is fastest.
The temperature difference between the containers and the cooler bag is greatest at the start, and smallest at the end.

✓ **Reasoning**

A bigger temperature difference means a greater rate of energy transfer: the containers cool and the air heats up more quickly at the start.

> How and why does the gradient change?

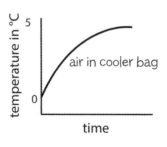

b) The air in the cooler bag must warm up to 5 °C because that is the final cola temperature. When both are at the same temperature, no more energy is transferred.
Energy will be transferred until the bag reaches the same temperature as the cola. The steepest gradient is at the start when the temperature difference is greatest.

Your turn

1

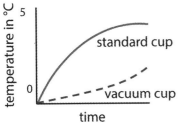

thermometer strip   air gap in wall of cup

standard cup   vacuum cup

Coffee at 80 °C is poured into a standard cup and a vacuum cup. The temperatures are measured by thermometer strips on the outside surface of each cup.

The graph shows how the temperatures of the two cups change with time
a) Explain the shape of the graphs.
b) Sketch a temperature-time graph to show how the temperature of the coffee changes in the standard cup.

2

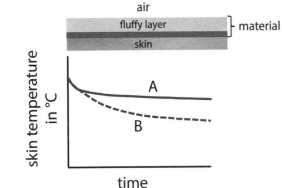

A new sportswear top is made of two layers. It can be worn with the fluffy layer on the outside or next to the skin. The graphs show how skin temperature changes when wearing the top both ways round.
Which graph shows the fluffy layer on the outside? Explain your choice.

3

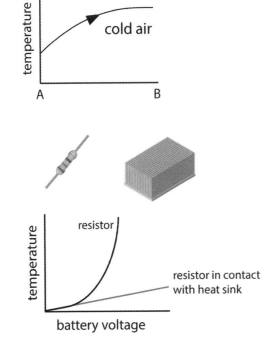

heat exchanger

warm air   clothes dryer

cold air   A   B

A clothes dryer has a heat exchanger. A warm stream of air from the dryer flows into the heat exchanger. It meets a stream of cold air entering from outside.
The graph shows the temperature of the cold air as it passes through the heat exchanger.
Explain why the graph is steepest at A.

A piece of metal with lots of thin conducting fins can be attached to some electrical components to keep them cool. It is called a 'heat sink'.
The graphs show how the temperature of a resistor changes with different voltages, with and without a heat sink.
Explain how the design and material of the heat sink fins stops the resistor overheating.

4

resistor

resistor in contact with heat sink

battery voltage

| **1** | /3 | **2** | /3 | **3** | /3 | **4** | /3 | Total | /12 |

Example

2.3 Specific heat capacity

An electric milk warmer heats 25 g milk from 4 °C to 60 °C. It transfers 7.8 kJ of energy from the mains but is only 70 % efficient.

How much energy does it take to heat 1 kg of the milk by 1 °C?

 Detect

✓ Diagram

✓ Values

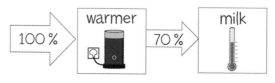

70% of the energy is passed on to the milk.

The mass of milk is 25 g and needs to be in kg.

We know 7800 J is transferred to the warmer.

The change in temperature of the milk = (60-4) = 56 °C.

✓ Unknown

I need to find the energy to heat 1 kg of a material by 1 °C, its specific heat capacity, c.

✓ Concept

The question is about specific heat capacity, I need an equation that links c to energy, mass and temperature.

⚙ **Recall**

1. How to find find energy using specific heat capacity.

Method 1: Scale the energy for a different mass and temperature.

A 1 kg mass takes c Joules of energy for a rise in temperature of 1 °C.

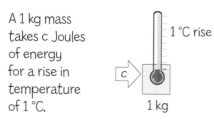

A 10 °C rise in temperature takes 1 × 10 = 10 times as much energy.

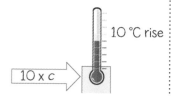

> What mass and temperature change does c give the energy required?

A 2 kg mass rise takes 2 × the energy (2 × c Joules) for a rise in temperature of 1 °C.

A 10°C rise in temperature takes 2 × 10 = 20 times as much energy for a 2 kg mass.

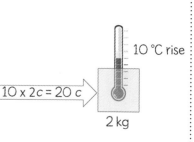

Method 2: Use the specific heat capacity equation.

I can find unknown quantities by changing the subject of the equation.

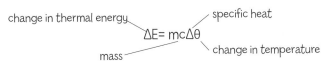

change in thermal energy — specific heat

$$\Delta E = mc\Delta\theta$$

mass — change in temperature

To remove the $\Delta\theta$, divide both sides by $\Delta\theta$.

$\Delta E = mc\Delta\theta$
$\div\Delta\theta \qquad \div\Delta\theta$

➡

$$\frac{\Delta E}{\Delta\theta} = mc$$

To remove the m, divide both sides by m.

$\frac{\Delta E}{\Delta\theta} = mc$
$\div m \qquad \div m$

➡

$$\frac{\Delta E}{m\Delta\theta} = c$$

2. How to calculate energy using efficiency.

$$\frac{\overset{?}{\Delta E}}{\underset{\checkmark\ \checkmark}{m\Delta\theta}} = c$$

I need the energy transferred to the milk.
I know the input energy (7.8 kJ) and efficiency (70%).
I can use this equation: $\text{Efficiency} = \dfrac{(\text{useful output energy})}{(\text{input energy})}$

 Solve

First I calculate the energy from the equation: $\text{Efficiency} = \dfrac{(\text{useful output energy})}{(\text{input energy})}$

Efficiency x input energy = useful output energy
70% efficiency is 0.7 as a fraction of 1
0.7 x 7800 J = 5460 J

Then I calculate the specific heat capacity.
Method 1: Scale the energy for a different mass and temperature.

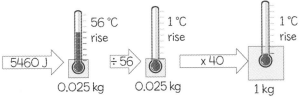

| 56 °C rise | 1 °C rise | 1 °C rise |

5460 J → 0.025 kg ÷ 56 → 0.025 kg x 40 → 1 kg

This is the energy to heat the 25 g of milk by 56 °C.

To find the energy for a 1°C rise, I divide by 56.
5460 J ÷ 56 = 97.5 J/ °C

I need the energy for 1 kg which is 40 x 25 g. So I multiply the energy by 40.
97.5 J x 40 = 3900 J/ °C

2. How to calculate energy using efficiency.

$$\Delta E = mc\Delta\theta$$

$$\frac{\Delta E}{m\Delta\theta} = c$$

I know:
E = 5460 J
m = 0.025 kg
$\Delta\theta$ = 60-4 = 56 °C

$$\frac{5460}{0.025 \times 56} = c$$

c = 3900 J/(kg °C)

So, the specific heat capacity, c = 3900 J/(kg °C)

> Can you identify the steps: rearrange, insert values?

Your turn

1

A glue gun heats 1 g of glue from 20 °C to 120 °C. It draws 200 J from the mains supply but it is only 55 % efficient. Find the specific heat capacity of the glue.

2

A mug containing 250 g water is heated in a 750 W microwave for 1 minute. It absorbs 45 000 J of energy.

What is the temperature increase, $\Delta\theta$?
(specific heat capacity of water = 4200 J/(kg °C))

3

A 0.3 kg baking potato is put in a BBQ with the lid on. It takes 81 000 J to heat the potato to its cooking temperature from 20 °C.

What is its cooking temperature?
The specific heat capacity of potato is 1700 J/(kg°C).

4

A handwarmer pouch contains gel at 40 °C. When it cools to 15 °C outdoors, it gives off 10.5 kJ of energy.

What is the mass of the gel?
The specific heat capacity of the gel is 3000 J/(kg °C).

1 /3 **2** /3 **3** /3 **4** /3 Total /12 © Mastery Science 2018

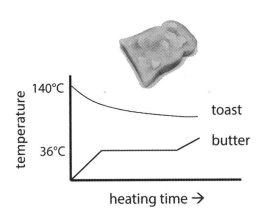

Example

2.4 Latent heat

5 g of butter is spread on hot toast and melts.
The latent heat of fusion of butter is 60 000 J/kg.
a) Calculate the energy transferred to the butter at its melting point.
b) The graph shows how the temperatures of the butter and toast change.
Explain why the butter remains at constant temperature while the toast is cooling down.

🔍 Detect

✓ Values

✓ Unknown

✓ Diagram

✓ Unknown

✓ Concept

a) The question gives the energy to melt 1 kg.

I need to know what proportion of the 60 000 J/kg of energy will be needed to melt only 0.005 kg (5g) of butter.

b) I need to explain what is happening to the butter when its temperature is constant, and why this process makes the toast cool.

The question is about energy: latent heat. I will need an equation to calculate the energy.

⚙️ Recall

1. How to calculate energy transfer for a state change.

Method 1: Scale the "energy to melt 1 kg" for a different mass.
L_{fus} is the specific latent heat of fusion, because the toast is melting.

> How do you convert 5 g into kg?

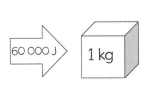

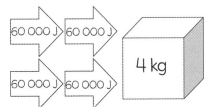

We know 60 000 J is needed to melt 1 kg.

If the mass is 4 × bigger, 4 × more energy is needed.

If the mass is 0.25 kg (¼ kg), only 0.25 (¼) of the energy is needed.

Method 2: Use the latent heat equation.

Thermal energy change for a change of state = mass × specific latent heat

$$E = mL_{fus}$$

Recall

2. How energy is transferred during a change of state.

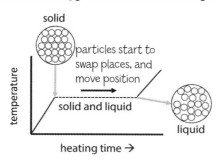

In the flat part of the graph, butter still absorbs energy. It does not speed up the particles (kinetic energy), but changes the arrangement of particles (potential energy) as solid butter turns to liquid. From liquid → gas, latent heat of vapourisation allows particles to break free completely.

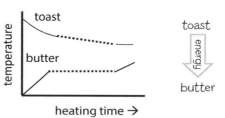

The energy needed to melt the butter comes from the toast, which is at a higher temperature.

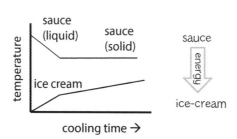

The process works in reverse for freezing e.g. an ice-cream sauce that goes solid. The sauce releases energy when it solidifies to the ice-cream which is at a lower temperature.

 Solve

a) Method 1: Scale the energy for a different mass.

  0.005 kg

5g = 0.005 kg. If 60 000 J are needed to melt 1 kg then 0. 005 × 60 000 J = 300 J are needed to melt 5g.

Method 2: Use latent heat equation.

E= mL
E = 0.005 kg × 60 000 J/kg
E = 300 J

b) When the temperature of butter is constant (36 °C), the butter is melting. In the solid, butter particles vibrate in fixed positions. At the melting point, added heat gives the particles enough energy to break away from their fixed positions and swap places with their neighbours. In the liquid state, particles now move past each other to new positions. Their potential energy increases instead of their kinetic energy.
The average kinetic energy of the particles does not change. This means the temperature does not increase.

Energy flows from regions of higher to lower temperature, so the energy to melt the butter comes from the hot toast. This causes the toast to cool.

1

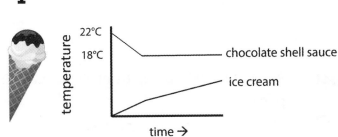

When 2 g of chocolate shell sauce is poured on to ice cream, it hardens. The latent heat of fusion is 105 kJ/kg.

a) Find the energy transferred from the sauce while it is freezing.

b) Explain why the ice cream gets warmer as the chocolate sauce sets.

2

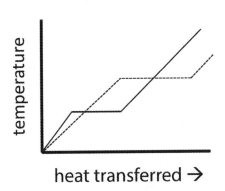

Use the data below to find the latent heat of vapourisation for ethanol and propanone.
Add labels to the graph to identify which trace is for which substance.

	Ethanol	Propanone
Energy (J) to vapourise 0.25 kg	211.5	129.5
L_{vap} (J/kg)		

3

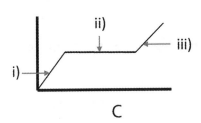

Gold is used to coat the mirror for a space telescope. 1 g of gold is vapourised to form a coating 100 nm thick. The latent heat of vapourisation of gold is 67 000 J/kg.

a) Calculate the energy supplied to the gold to vapourise it.

b) Name the state(s) gold is in at each point i), ii) and iii).

4 The flow of steam from a stream cleaner is 0.005 kg per second.
The steam condenses, transferring its energy to loosen dirt and kill bacteria. The latent heat of vaporisation of steam is 2260 kJ/kg.

a) How much energy due to condensation of steam is delivered per second?

b) Explain which graph shows this.

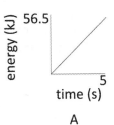
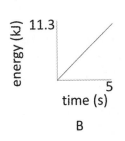
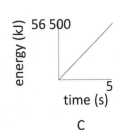

A   B   C

| **1** | /3 | **2** | /3 | **3** | /3 | **4** | /3 | Total | /12 |

2.5 Pressure in a gas

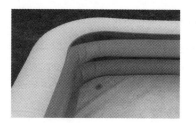

Pool inflated

Pool not inflated

Anna uses a bike pump to inflate her paddling pool.

a) As she pumps air in, the walls become firmer. Explain why this happens.

b) The pool is left out on a sunny day and the walls become even harder.
Explain why this happens.

✔ Diagram
✔ Values
✔ Unknown
✔ Concept

🖐 Detect

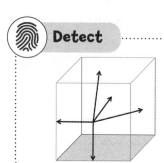

a) I know the walls get firmer when there is more air inside.
b) I need to explain what increases this force on the walls.

The question is about the particle model, force and pressure.

⚙ Recall

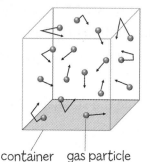

container   gas particle

1. How particle energy depends on temperature.

In the particle model of a gas:
- air particles are in constant random motion.
- the average kinetic energy of the particles is proportional to the temperature of the gas.
Therefore, at higher temperatures, particles move faster.

2. How particle collisions with a surface create pressure.

Air particle collides with surface.

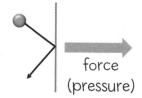

force (pressure)

It exerts a force at right angles to the wall.

At any given moment, there are a large number of particles colliding with each unit area of wall. The pressure is the total force of all the collisions in any given moment, per unit area of wall. It is the same in all directions.

Recall

Why does kinetic energy increase when temperature increases?

3. How pressure changes with temperature.

cooler air

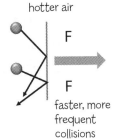
hotter air

faster, more frequent collisions

The size of the pressure depends on how often particles hit the walls, and how fast they are going.

A faster collision means a particle exerts more force on the wall.
More frequent collisions means more total force per unit area at any moment.

4. How atmospheric pressure works.

Atmospheric pressure acts inwards.

Air particles collide with the walls producing a force inwards, from all directions.

Internal pressure acts outwards.

The net force on the walls depends on whether the atmospheric pressure or the internal pressure is bigger.

 Solve

✓ Claim

✓ Evidence

✓ Reasoning

Why does pumping air in increase the collisions?

✓ Claim

✓ Evidence

✓ Reasoning

Student Workbook not to be photocopied

a) The walls of the pool get firmer as air is pumped in because the extra air increases the pressure on the walls.

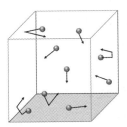

Particles in a gas move fast and collide with the walls. Each collision produces a force. The pressure is the size of the force on each unit area of wall.
Pumping in air means putting more air particles inside. This produces more collisions and more force per unit area at any moment. So the pressure on the wall increases and the walls feel hard.

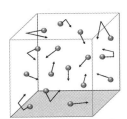

b) The walls of the pool get harder on a hot day because when the temperature increases the pressure from the air inside increases.
Radiation from the sun causes the temperature of the air to increase as particles absorb the energy and move faster.

They collide more often with the walls and hit the wall harder, exerting more force. So the total force on a unit area at any moment increases. Therefore the pressure increases and makes the walls feel even harder.

1

The pressure in a balloon drops after a few days.
a) Explain why.
b) The pressure in the balloon drops even more when placed in a freezer. Explain why.

2

An aerosol spray can is printed with this safety instruction:
"Pressurised container: Do not expose to temperatures exceeding 50°C."
Explain using the particle model why the temperature should not exceed 50°C.

3

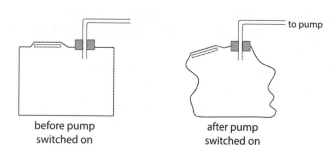

before pump
switched on

to pump

after pump
switched on

Freddie removes all the air from a can by connecting it to a vacuum pump. The can collapses.

Use the idea of pressure to explain why this happens.

4

A driver pushes hard on the brakes to make an emergency stop. The pressure inside the tyres increases. Explain why.

1 /3   **2** /3   **3** /3   **4** /3   Total /12

2.6 Liquid pressure

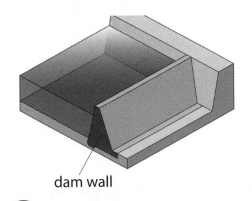

dam wall

A dam is a concrete structure designed to hold back water.

The diagram shows its cross-section. Explain why you think the dam wall has this shape.

 Detect

✓ **Values**

✓ **Unknown**

✓ **Concept**

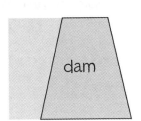

dam

The diagram shows that the dam is thicker at the bottom compared to the top.

I need to explain how its design allows it to hold back a high column of water and how this relates to it being thicker at the bottom.

This question is about pressure in a liquid.

 Recall

plastic bag   small holes

water comes out in all directions

pressure acts in all directions

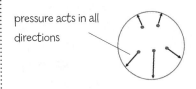

tall cylinder

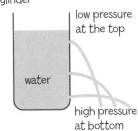

water

low pressure at the top

high pressure at bottom

1. How a fluid exerts a pressure on a surface.

The water spurts out in all directions.

So the particles inside must be exerting a force on the bag.

The total force on a given area of the bag is called fluid pressure.

2. How pressure in a fluid changes with depth.

The pressure at the bottom of the cylinder makes water spurt out faster. Pressure increases with depth.

Think of the pressure as the weight of the column of particles above it pushing down. The further down an object goes in a liquid, the bigger the column of particles above it. So the pressure gets bigger.

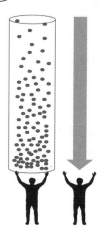

3. How air exerts a pressure on objects.

Air particles, like those in a liquid, push on surfaces.

Think of the atmospheric pressure on Earth as the weight of a column of air particles as high as the atmosphere pushing down on you.

Why does atmospheric pressure get smaller with increasing altitude?

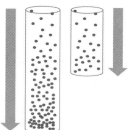

4. How atmospheric pressure changes with altitude.

The higher up an object goes in the atmosphere, the smaller the weight of the column of particles that is on top pushing down.

So atmospheric pressure reduces with altitude.

atmospheric pressure

liquid pressure

Under the surface of a liquid, atmospheric pressure adds to the pressure of the liquid.

Solve

☑ **Claim**

I think the walls of the dam are made thicker at the bottom because the pressure of the water they have to withstand is greater at the bottom.

☑ **Evidence**

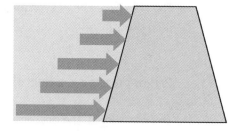

Water particles exert a force on the concrete. The total force on unit area is called the pressure. You can think of the pressure at any point under the water as the weight of the water particles above it pushing down. As the water gets deeper, there are more water particles above. So the weight and the pressure increase.

☑ **Reasoning**

To withstand the increased pressure from the water, the dam walls are designed to be thicker at the bottom.

Your turn

1

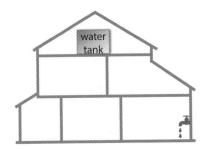

Water tanks are usually placed at the top of buildings.
Explain why.

2

When you take a packet of crisps on an aeroplane it inflates.
Explain why this happens.

3

The bends is a dangerous condition that divers can experience. It happens at the end of a deep dive if the external pressure drops too quickly.

a) Explain what a diver can do at the end of a dive to avoid getting the bends.
b) If a diver gets the bends, why could the condition get worse if they are airlifted to hospital?

4

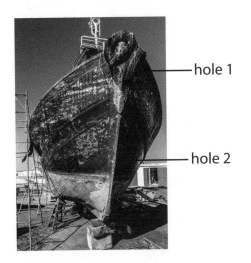

hole 1

hole 2

A fisherman notices two similar size holes in his boat.
Which one should he fix first? Explain your choice.

3.1 Transverse & longitudinal

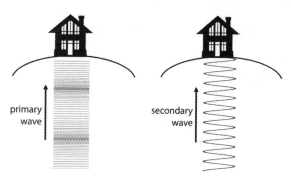

primary wave

secondary wave

The diagram shows two types of wave that travel from earthquakes through the Earth.

For each wave, describe:

a) How particles in the Earth move relative to the direction the wave travels.

b) How the house will move when the waves hit the surface.

 Detect

- ✓ Concept
- ✓ Values
- ✓ Unknown

The question is about two types of wave: transverse and longitudinal.

a) For the primary wave, the parallel lines show areas where waves are closer and further apart. For the secondary wave, the lines show a back and forth wave motion.
I need to work out which type of wave each diagram represents.
b) I need to work out how each wave motion is transferred to the house.

 Recall

1. How a wave transfers energy.

droplet makes water vibrate

A wave is started by a vibration. Energy spreads out from the site of vibration.
But the things that vibrate do not move along, they only go back and forth.

2. How particles move in a transverse wave.

particle movement

wave movement

Particles in solids and on the surface of water carry transverse waves.

Particles move at 90° (right angles) to the wave. Energy is transferred in the direction that the wave travels.

Light is a transverse wave that does not involve particles. An electric field vibrates at right angles to the wave direction.

3. How particles move in a longitudinal wave.

Longitudinal waves travel as a series of pulses.

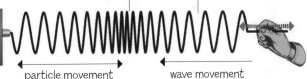

high pressure: particles close together

low pressure: particles further apart

← particle movement →   ← wave movement

Particles move in the same direction as the wave. Energy is also transferred in the direction of the wave.

As particles vibrate back and forth from their equilibrium (average) position, they collide with their neighbours and pass on the pulse.

Sound travels as a longitudinal wave through gases, liquids and solids.

compression: particles close together

rarefaction: particles further apart

Particles can be air particles or particles in solids or liquids.

4. How sound can be visualised as a wave pattern.

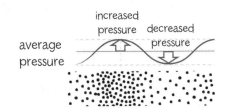

increased pressure   decreased pressure

average pressure

The up and down pattern shows how the pressure changes along a sound wave.

Solve

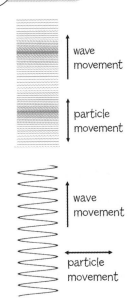

wave movement

particle movement

wave movement

particle movement

Primary wave
a) The diagram shows particles vibrating in the same direction as the wave moves. It is a longitudinal wave. Particles collide with neighbouring particles and pass on the vibrations as compression pulses.
b) The energy is passed to the house, where the wave tries to move the walls up and down.

Secondary wave
a) The diagram shows particles vibrating at right angles to the wave movement and the direction of energy transfer. It is a transverse wave. Particles pass on their side-to-side movement to their neighbours.
b) The motion shakes the foundations and walls of the house sideways.

Hint p.121

1 cleaning chairs

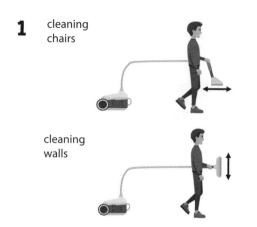

cleaning walls

Alan uses a vacuum cleaner with an elastic extension tube. For each diagram explain:

a) What type of wave his movement sets up in the extension tube.

b) How energy is transferred along the tube.

2

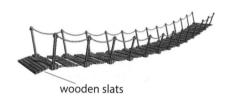

wooden slats

Some children play on a rope bridge made of wooden slats. They make waves in three different ways:

a) Jumping up and down at one end

b) Swinging one end from side to side

c) Pulling 5 slats towards one end of the bridge, then letting go.

Explain which type of wave each movement sets up.

3

microphone diaphragm (a sheet of metal that can vibrate)

displacement of diaphragm

time

The diagram shows how air particles cause a microphone diaphragm to vibrate.

The oscilloscope shows how the displacement of the diaphragm changes.

Explain the shape of the pattern using the idea of longitudinal waves.

4

A diving bird splashes into a lake. A frog at the edge of the lake feels the ripples and a fish detects the noise.

Explain why the two animals experience different types of wave.

Example

3.2 Wave properties

The diagrams show how a tuning fork vibrates and affects the air around it.

a) Find the period, frequency and wavelength of the sound waves. Note: the diagrams are not to scale.

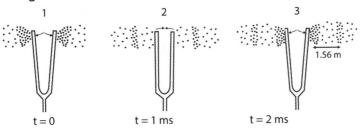

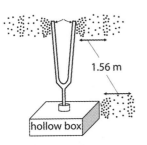

b) This diagram shows what happens when the tuning fork is put on a hollow box.

Explain which features of the sound change and which remain the same.

 Detect

✓ **Values**

The prong moves in and out, making air particles squash together and spread apart. The distance between similar areas is 1.56 m and the time for it to go back and forth is 2 milliseconds.

The question is about wave properties.

✓ **Concept**
✓ **Unknown**

a) I need to find the wavelength, period, and frequency.
b) I need to work out whether or not these change with the hollow box.

Recall

1. Wavelength is the distance between compressions or rarefactions.

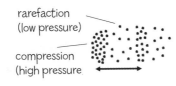

The wavelength is the distance between two identical regions e.g. from the middle of one compression to the middle of the next.

> How does each particle move?

2. Period is the time for a complete oscillation.

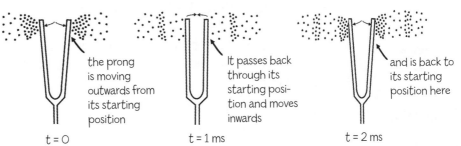

The period is also the time for a complete wave to pass a point.

3. Frequency is the number of waves produced per second.
It is also the number of waves that go by in 1 s. Frequency gives sound its pitch.

Frequency, f, is the inverse of period.
Why? Imagine it takes ½ s for a complete vibration.
That means in 1 s, there are 2 waves produced. So the frequency is 2 Hz.

Period = 1/frequency   T = 1/f   Or f = 1/T

4. How loudness depends on the amplitude of the vibration.
Amplitude means how far particles are displaced from their average positions.

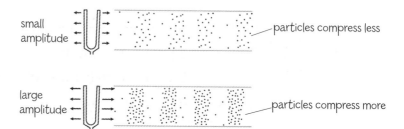

small amplitude — particles compress less

large amplitude — particles compress more

 Solve

If frequency increases, what happens to the period?

a) Wavelength: This is the distance between compressions or rarefactions.
It is 1.56 m.

Period: This is the time for the prongs to go through one complete oscillation, between pictures 1 and 3. So the period is 2 ms = 0.002 s.

Frequency: This is the number of oscillations per second. It is the inverse of the period:

$$f = 1/T = 1/0.002$$
$$f = 500 \text{ Hz.}$$

✓ **Claim**

✓ **Evidence**
✓ **Reasoning**

✓ **Evidence**
✓ **Reasoning**

b) When the tuning fork is on the hollow box, the wavelength, frequency and pitch of the sound stay the same, but the amplitude (volume) increases.

The hollow box vibrates with the tuning fork and it pushes the air too. This increases the amplitude of the wave by making the air particles travel further each oscillation. This makes the sound louder.

The hollow box does not change how the tuning fork vibrates back and forth. So the frequency and wavelength of the sound stay the same, and therefore so does its pitch.

1 In a swimming pool, a machine makes waves by driving a ball up and down.

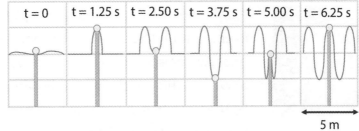

5 m

Find the period, frequency and wavelength of the water waves produced.

2

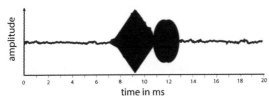

Scientists study the calls of bats by visualising the waves.

a) This is an amplitude-time graph of the bat calls. Describe how the movement of air particles changes between 7 and 11 ms.

b) This is a frequency-time graph of the bat calls. Describe how the period changes with time.

3 Fish return to a coral reef every year by following sounds from the reef. The graph shows how the sounds vary. If a boat engine has a similar pitch to the reef, some fish follow it by mistake.

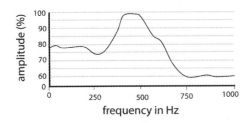

Boat engine	Period of sound wave in ms
Mega Motor	2.2
Shark Surf	1.9
Speeder	1.1

Explain which engine(s) could be confusing the fish.

4 The diagram shows two waves from an earthquake. One moves on the surface of the land and is transverse. The p-wave travels through the rock below the surface. Its compressions are shown as shaded areas on the diagram.

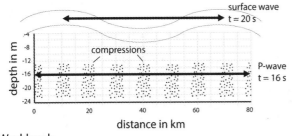

a) Find the wavelength and frequency of each wave.

b) The amplitude of the surface wave is 2 m while the p-wave amplitude is microscopic. Explain why surface waves cause far more damage to buildings.

3.3 Wave speed equation

A swimmer uses a device that beeps regularly to keep her strokes even. In lap 1 it beeps at 440 Hz and the wavelength of the sound underwater is 3.4 m. In lap 2 it beeps at 660 Hz.

a) What is the wavelength of the lap 2 beep?

b) The beep travels through her head to her inner ear. Lap 1 beeps have a wavelength of 8.4 m in bone. What is the speed of sound in bone?

Detect

✓ **Values**

✓ **Unknown**

✓ **Concept/skill**

	v in m/s	λ in m	f in Hz
Lap 1	?	3.4	440
Lap 2	?	?	660

The table shows the values and unknowns.

a) I need to find the wavelength of the lap 2 beep.
The question is about wave properties, and the skill of using the wave equation.

✓ **Diagram**

✓ **Unknown**

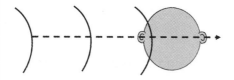

b) In the swimmer's skull, the lap 1 wavelength increases to 8.4 m.
I need to find the speed of sound in bone.

Recall

1. How the frequency of a sound is fixed by the source.

device makes a fixed number of waves per second

the same number of peaks travel past each point each second

Frequency means the number of waves that pass a point per second.

Even when the wave passes from one material (water) into another (swimmer's ear bone), the same number of waves still pass a point per second. The frequency stays the same.

2. How wave speed, wavelength and frequency are related.

The equation is: speed = wavelength x frequency

$$v = \lambda f$$

The equation can be changed to make f the subject:

divide both sides by the wavelength

$v = \lambda f$

$\div \lambda \quad \div \lambda$

$f = \dfrac{v}{\lambda}$

3. How the speed of sound waves changes in different materials.

In any material, the speed of a wave is the same at all frequencies.
But the speed changes in different materials and in different states.

speed of waves increase

solid

liquid

gas

Densely packed particles pass the wave on quickly as they collide with each other.

Particles are in loose contact with each other and swap places. So the wave is not passed on as quickly.

Sound travels slowest in a gas because particle collisions happen less often.

4) How changing a wave's speed changes its wavelength.

A wave changes speed when it passes into a different material.

if speed increases, this side of the equation is bigger

$v{\uparrow} = \lambda{\uparrow} \times f$ (same)

so this side of the equation must also be bigger

So if the speed in another material increases, wavelength increases (and if speed decreases, wavelength decreases).

material 1: slow speed, small wavelength

material 2: fast speed, big wavelength

Wave speed is directly proportional to wavelength: $v = \lambda f$
Wave speed is also directly proportional to frequency: $v = \lambda \mathbf{f}$

 Solve

a) Wavelength of lap 2 beep. I only know f but I know two quantities for lap 1.
So I can use the wave equation to find v.

	v in m/s	λ in m	f in Hz
Lap 1	?	3.4	440
Lap 2	?	?	660

Lap 1: $v = \lambda f$
$v = 3.4\text{ m} \times 440\text{ Hz} = 1496\text{ m/s}$
v is the same for both beeps.
So I can use v calculated from lap 1 to find λ for lap 2.

Lap 2: $v = \lambda f$
$1496\text{ m/s} = \lambda \times \times 660\text{ Hz}$
$\lambda = \dfrac{v}{f} = \dfrac{1496}{660} = 2.3\text{ m}$

b) Wave speed in bone. I know the wavelength = 8.4 m. Sounds travels at different speeds in different materials, but the frequency doesn't change. Therefore it is still 440 Hz.

$v = \lambda f = 8.4\text{ m} \times 440\text{ Hz} = 3696\text{ m/s}$, the speed of sound in bone.

Your turn

1 Tara sings a note of frequency 880 Hz, which has a wavelength of 0.39 m.
a) Find the wavelength of a 220 Hz note.
b) She inhales a mouthful of helium gas and sings the higher pitched note again. The new wavelength is 1.03 m.

Calculate the speed of sound in helium.

2 A sound with a 1.30 m wavelength travels along a metal pipeline at 1300 m/s. Then it travels through air at 344 m/s, where its wavelength is 0.344 m.
a) Find the frequency of sound in each material.
b) Explain why the two frequencies are the same or different.

3

A car alarm makes two notes, one 622 Hz and the other 520 Hz. The alarm goes off when the car is buried under snow. The lower note has a wavelength in snow of 1.8 m.
a) Calculate the speed of sound in snow.
b) Calculate the wavelength of the higher note.

4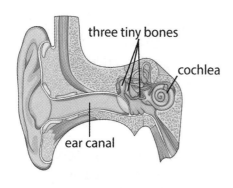

three tiny bones

cochlea

ear canal

When sound passes from air into the bones of the ear, its speed changes.
Complete the table to show what happens to the frequency and wavelength of a 300 Hz sound when it reaches the ear.

	Ear canal	Bones	Cochlea
Speed in m/s	344	3700	1500
Frequency in Hz	330		
Wavelength in m			

1 /3 **2** /3 **3** /3 **4** /3 **Total** /12 © Mastery Science 2018

4.1 Represent subatomic particles

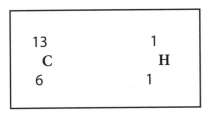

13		1
C		H
6		1

a) An isotope of carbon has a mass number of 13. Draw an atom of the isotope to show the subatomic particles with their charge.

b) In a star, a nucleus of the carbon-13 isotope fuses with a hydrogen nucleus (mass number 1) to form a bigger nucleus. Name the isotope formed.

 Detect

The question tells me that the atom is carbon and the mass number is 13. The subatomic particles in an atom are protons, neutrons and electrons.

I need to work out how many of each particle are in the atom so I can draw it.

I need to work out what element is formed when a hydrogen-1 nucleus fuses with the nucleus of a carbon-13 atom.

This question is about how to use information to find out the number of subatomic particles in an atom and how to draw one to show where they are located.

✓ **Values**

✓ **Unknown**

✓ **Concept**

 Recall

1. How the properties of subatomic particles differ.

Subatomic particle	Charge	Mass
Proton	+1	1
Neutron	0 (neutral)	1
Electron	-1	Very small

Subatomic particles are parts of the atom. They have different masses and charges.

2. How to model the subatomic particles in an atom.

A model of an atom shows a central nucleus orbited by electrons.

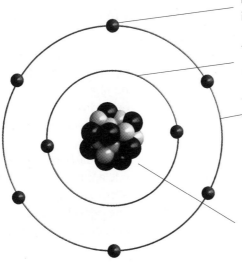

Electrons orbit the nucleus. They are arranged in different shells (energy levels).

The innermost shell (lowest energy) is filled first. It can hold 2 electrons.

The next two shells can each hold 8 electrons. The electronic configuration means the number of electrons in each shell. In this atom it is 2, 6.

The nucleus contains protons and neutrons. It has an overall positive charge, which attracts the electrons.

3. How to work out atomic numbers and mass numbers.

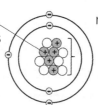

atomic number =
number of protons
= 5

mass number = number of protons
= 5 + 6   + number of neutrons
= 11

Atoms have zero overall charge
because the number of (-) electrons
equals the number of (+) protons

mass number = 11
Boron
atomic number = 5

> **How many protons (and electrons) do all carbon atoms have?**

11	12	14	16
B	**C**	**N**	**O**
boron 5	carbon 6	nitrogen 7	oxygen 8

atomic number

The periodic table shows 'relative atomic mass' not mass number.

Atoms have different isotopes with different numbers of neutrons and different mass numbers. Relative atomic mass is an average.

 Solve

✓ Claim

✓ Evidence

✓ Reasoning

> **How many particles of each type do the isotopes have?**

✓ Claim

✓ Evidence

✓ Reasoning

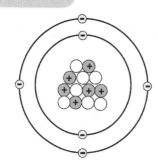

a) Here is an atom of the carbon isotope. I know its mass number is 13 and the periodic table shows its atomic number is 6.

From the mass number, I know protons plus neutrons = 13. As it has 6 protons, there must be 13 - 6 = 7 neutrons.

Atoms are neutral, so there must be 6 electrons. Electrons are arranged in shells. The first can hold two electrons. The other 4 electrons go into the second shell.

carbon-13 nucleus   hydrogen-1 nucleus   nitrogen-14 nucleus

b) The isotope formed is nitrogen-14.

The periodic table shows hydrogen's atomic number is 1, and the question says its mass number is 1.
So hydrogen has 1 proton and 0 neutrons, as mass number (protons + neutrons) = 1.

When carbon-13 joins with hydrogen-1, the nucleus has 7 protons and 7 neutrons. Its atomic number is 7 and mass number is 14. The periodic table shows me this is an isotope of nitrogen, nitrogen-14.

1   A isotope of nitrogen has a mass number of 15.

    a) Draw an atom of this isotope showing the subatomic particles and their charge.

    b) In a star, the nucleus of this isotope fuses with the nucleus of a hydrogen atom with mass number 1. The result is a nucleus of a new isotope plus a helium nucleus with a mass number of 4. Name the new isotope.

2   A magnesium atom, atomic number 12 loses all its outer electrons. It is now a charged particle called an ion.

    Explain what the charge of the magnesium ion is.

3

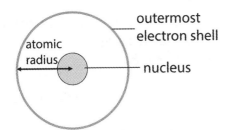

A fluorescent tube light contains a mixture of neon and argon.

Which element in the mixture has the bigger atomic radius?

Explain your choice in terms of atomic structure.

4

Heavy water molecules look like normal water but contain a different isotope of hydrogen.

Use the information to draw an atom of the hydrogen isotope in heavy water. Show all the sub-atomic particles.

Sum of atomic masses of elements	
Normal water	Heavy water
18	20

 **Example**

4.2 Calculate relative atomic mass

The magnesium in a food supplement contains three isotopes with different amounts (abundances):

$^{24}_{12}$**Mg** $^{25}_{12}$**Mg** $^{26}_{12}$**Mg**

80%   **10%**   **10%**

a) A student writes: 'The relative atomic mass of magnesium is 24.0'.
   Why is this wrong?
b) Calculate the correct relative atomic mass.

Detect

✓ **Diagram**

✓ **Values**

✓ **Unknown**

✓ **Concept**

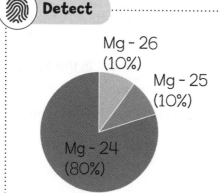

Mg – 26 (10%)
Mg – 25 (10%)
Mg – 24 (80%)

The sample of magnesium contains three isotopes. They have the same atomic number but a different mass number.

I know that most of the magnesium is in the form Mg-24.
I need to explain why the relative atomic mass is not 24.0.

This question is about calculating the relative atomic mass of a group of isotopes.

Recall

1. How isotopes of the same element differ.

Isotopes have the same number of protons and electrons but a different number of neutrons.

— more neutrons = higher mass number

$^{24}_{12}$**Mg** $^{25}_{12}$**Mg** $^{26}_{12}$**Mg**

same atomic number = same element

Why do isotopes have different masses?

protons = 12	protons = 12	protons = 12
electrons = 12	electrons = 12	electrons = 12
neutrons = 12	neutrons = 13	neutrons = 14

Isotopes have the same number of protons and electrons but a different number of neutrons.

2. How to calculate relative atomic mass with averages.

When an atom has different isotopes relative atomic mass, A_r, gives an average mass based on how abundant each one is. I can calculate A_r using a 'weighted' average.

> **How do you calculate average mass?**

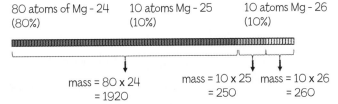

Suppose there are 3 atoms of magnesium, one of each isotope.

The total mass = 24 + 25 + 26 = 75
The average, A_r = 75/3 = 25

80 atoms of Mg – 24 (80%)	10 atoms Mg – 25 (10%)	10 atoms Mg – 26 (10%)

mass = 80 x 24 = 1920

mass = 10 x 25 = 250

mass = 10 x 26 = 260

But the amounts (abundances) of each magnesium isotope are not equal.
Suppose there are 100 Mg atoms. The percentage abundances become whole numbers.

To find the average, add up the masses (1920+250+260 = 2430) and then divide by 100 (2430÷100), and the average, A_r, is 24.3.

3. How to calculate relative atomic mass with an equation.

The weighted average can be turned into an equation:

> **What sum should I use to answer the question?**

$$A_r = \frac{\overset{\text{isotope 1}}{(\text{mass no.} \times \text{abundance})} + \overset{\text{Isotope 2}}{(\text{mass no.} \times \text{abundance})} + \overset{\text{Isotope 3}}{(\text{mass no.} \times \text{abundance})}}{100}$$

a) The relative atomic mass of magnesium is not 24.0 because that is the mass of only one isotope. Relative atomic mass is a weighted average mass. It is based on the abundances of the different isotopes. Magnesium has three isotopes, each with a different atomic mass.

b) The supplement contains 3 magnesium isotopes. Each has a different abundance.

> **Why is the answer slightly bigger than 24.0?**

$$A_r = \frac{\overset{\text{Mg-24}}{(24 \times 80)} + \overset{\text{Mg-25}}{(25 \times 10)} + \overset{\text{Mg-26}}{(26 \times 10)}}{100}$$

← Multiply the mass of each isotope by its abundance

$$A_r = \frac{1920 + 250 + 260}{100}$$

← The total mass of these atoms

← To get the average value, divide by 100 atoms

$$A_r = \frac{2430}{100}$$

$$A_r = 24.3$$

So the relative atomic mass, A_r = 24.3.

Your turn

1

$^{28}_{14}$Si $^{29}_{14}$Si $^{30}_{14}$Si

92%   **5%**   **3%**

The silicon in a sample of glass is made of three isotopes with different abundances.

a) Alfie says that the relative atomic mass must be close to, but not exactly, 28.

Explain why he is correct.

b) Calculate the relative atomic mass of the silicon.

2

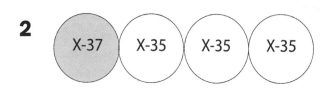

X-37   X-35   X-35   X-35

A sample of element X contains isotopes with mass numbers 37 and 35 in a ratio of 1:3.

Calculate the relative atomic mass of X.

3   The relative atomic mass of element Y is 80.

The element has two isotopes, which have mass numbers of 79 and 81.

In a 28 g sample of element Y, how much of each isotope would you expect to find? Explain your answer.

4

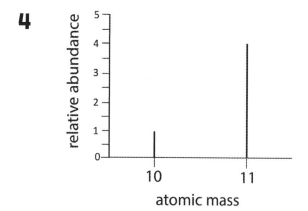

A mass spectrometer is an instrument that measures the relative abundance of isotopes in a sample.

The chart shows the mass spectrometer results for a sample of boron.

Calculate its relative atomic mass.

1 /3   **2** /3   **3** /3   **4** /3   Total   /12   © Mastery Science 2018

4.3 Periodic patterns

Boiling point	-185 °C
Conductivity	Does not conduct electricity
Reactivity	Does not react with hydrogen, oxygen or magnesium

In 1894 a new element was discovered. The table shows some data about it.

a) Would you place this element in group 1, 7 or 0 of the periodic table? Explain your reasons.

b) How many electrons do you expect the element has in its outer shell? Give a reason.

 Detect

✓ Values
✓ Unknown

✓ Concept

I know some properties of the new element.
a) I need to work out whether the new element belongs to group 1, 7 or 0 in the periodic table.
b) I need to think about how the electrons are arranged in the elements in this group.
This question is about how the properties of elements are linked to their position in the periodic table.

Recall

1. How elements are arranged in the periodic table.

Elements are placed in groups (columns) and periods (rows).

group → 1 2 .... 3 4 5 6 7 0

atomic number increases →

period (also number of electron shells) ↓

1	H						2	He
2	3 Li	4 Be				5 B	6 C	7 N	8 O	9 F	10 Ne
3	11 Na	12 Mg				13 Al	14 Si	15 P	16 S	17 Cl	18 Ar
4	19 K	20 Ca					
5							
6							

2. How group number is related to electrons in the outer shell.

For groups 1–7 the group number = how many electrons are in the outer shell.

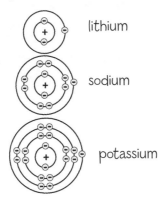

increase in number of electron shells ↓

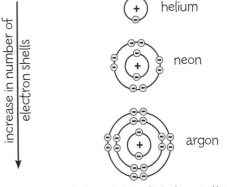

Group 1 elements all have 1 electron in their outer shell.

Group 0 elements have 8 electrons in their outer shell (apart from helium)

Having the same number of outer shell electrons leads to similar chemical properties.

Group 0 elements have a full outer shell - what does this mean?

3. How position in the periodic table relates to properties.

metals	• mostly high melting and boiling points • conduct electricity

non-metals	• low melting and boiling points • do not conduct electricity

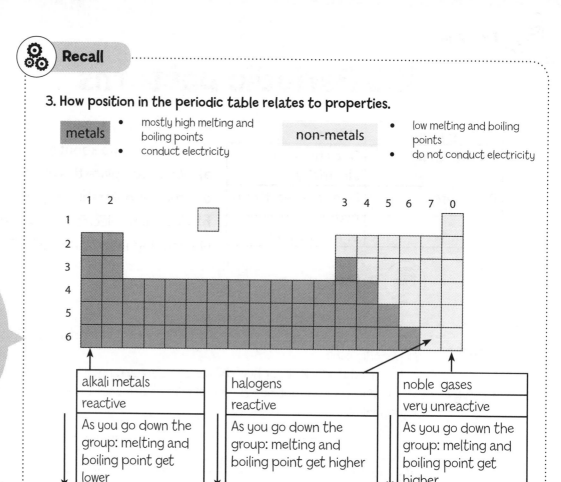

What properties would an element at the bottom of group 1 have?

alkali metals	halogens	noble gases
reactive	reactive	very unreactive
As you go down the group: melting and boiling point get lower	As you go down the group: melting and boiling point get higher	As you go down the group: melting and boiling point get higher

 Solve

✔ Claim

✔ Evidence
✔ Reasoning

✔ Claim
✔ Evidence
✔ Reasoning

a) First, the new element belongs on the far right of the periodic table, either in group 7 or group 0.
The element does not conduct electricity. It has a low boiling point.
Therefore it is a non-metal. Non-metals appear on the far right side of the table.

Of the two far right groups, I think the new element should be placed in group 0.
The element does not react with hydrogen, oxygen or magnesium.
It cannot be in group 7 because it does not form compounds with hydrogen and magnesium. Therefore it must be an unreactive noble gas from group 0.

b) Noble gases have a full outer shell of electrons. So I expect the new element to have 8 electrons, like most of the other group 0 elements.

Your turn

1

Melting point	-7.2 °C
Conductivity	Does not conduct electricity
Reactivity	Reacts slowly with calcium and hydrogen

In 1826 a new element was discovered. The table shows some data about it.
a) Suggest which group in the periodic table (1, 7 or 0) this element should be placed in. Explain your reasons.
b) Give the number of electrons in its outer shell.

2

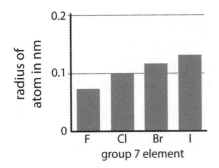

A simple model of an atom is a sphere with a radius.

radius

The graph shows a trend in the atomic radius of group 7 elements.
Give an explanation for the trend.

3

Element	Melting point in °C	Boiling point in °C	Colour
F	-220	-188	Yellow
Cl	-101	-35	Green
Br	-7	59	Orange/brown
I	114	184	Dark grey

The table shows the properties of the first four halogens.
Astatine (At) is found in group 7 below iodine.

Suggest the appearance and state of astatine at room temperature (25°C). Explain your answer.

4

Hydrogen is a reactive gas that can be burned as a fuel. Two students argue about hydrogen's position in the periodic table.
a) Tasha thinks it should be in group 1.
Give one piece of evidence that supports her claim and one piece against it.
b) Dina thinks it should be in group 7.
Give one piece of evidence to support her claim.

4.4 Reactions of groups 1 & 7

Element	When melted sodium is added
Bromine	Small orange sparks. A white powder is formed.
Chlorine	Very vigorous reaction, bright orange light. A white powder is formed.

A scientist reacted two different group 7 elements with sodium.

a) Name the product of each reaction.

b) Explain the difference in the reactions of bromine and chlorine with sodium.

 Detect

✓ **Values**

Both chlorine and bromine reacted to form a white powder. But the reaction of chlorine with sodium was more vigorous than the reaction of bromine.

✓ **Unknown**

a) I don't know the white powders formed in each reaction:

sodium + bromine → ?   sodium + chlorine → ?

b) I don't know why chlorine is more reactive than bromine.

✓ **Concept**

This question is about explaining trends in reactivity of group 1 and 7 elements.

 Recall

1. How group 1 elements (alkali metals) react.

Water:

metal + water → metal hydroxide + hydrogen

$2Na + 2H_2O →$ $2NaOH + H_2$

Group 7 elements (halogens):

metal + halogen → metal halide

$2Na + Cl_2 →$ $2NaCl$

Oxygen (when heated):

metal + oxygen → metal oxide

$2Na + O_2 →$ $2NaO$

2. How group 1 reactivity depends on electron structure.

All group 1 atoms have one electron on their outer shell. When they react, they lose this electron to form a positive ion.

sodium atom   sodium ion

atom loses an electron so ion has a +1 charge

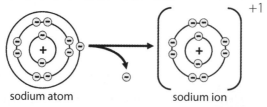

lithium - 2 shells

Sodium's outer electron is further from the positively charged nucleus than lithium's.

It feel less attraction, and is lost more easily.

Sodium is more reactive.

sodium - 3 shells

The easier it is for the atom to lose electrons from its outer shell, the more reactive it is.

Reactivity increases down group 1.

3. How group 7 elements (halogens) react.

Group 7 elements take part in displacement reactions.
chlorine + sodium bromide → sodium chloride + bromine
$$Cl_2 + 2NaBr → 2NaCl + Br_2$$
A more reactive halogen can displace a less reactive halogen from a solution of its salt.

4. How group 7 reactivity depends on electron structure.

All group 7 atoms have seven electrons on their outer shell. When they react with metals they gain an electron to form a negative ion with a charge of -1.

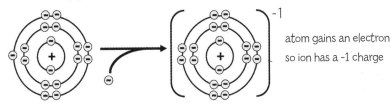

atom gains an electron so ion has a -1 charge

5. How electron structure affects group 7 reactivity
All group 7 atoms have seven electrons on their outer shell. When they react with metals they gain an electron to form a negative ion with a charge of -1.

chlorine - 3 shells

> What is the relationship between size and reactivity for the atoms in each group?

An electron added to chlorine's outer shell is closer to the nucleus than bromine's.
It feels more attraction, so it is added more easily.
Chlorine is more reactive.

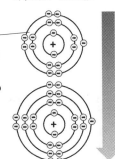

The easier it is for an atom to gain electrons, the more reactive it is.

Reactivity decreases down group 7.

bromine - 4 shells

💡 **Solve**

a) Group 1 metals react with group 7 elements like this:
metal + halogen → metal halide
so: sodium + bromine → sodium bromide   sodium + chlorine → sodium chloride.

✔ Claim
✔ Evidence

✔ Reasoning

b) Chlorine is a more reactive element than bromine.
When chlorine reacted with sodium a more vigorous reaction was observed.

This is because chlorine atoms gain an electron more easily than bromine atoms.
When group 7 elements react they gain an electron to fill their outer shell. The negative electron is attracted to the positive nucleus.
In chlorine the outer shell is closer to the nucleus so the force of attraction between the electron and the nucleus is greater than in bromine. So, it has a greater tendency to attract an electron.
This explains why chlorine is more reactive than bromine.

Your turn

1

Alkali metal	Observations during reaction
Lithium	The lithium melted to form a ball. It moved slowly around the surface of the water.
Sodium	The sodium melted to form a ball. It move very quickly around the surface of the water. It had an orange flame.

A teacher added two alkali metals to water. The table shows the observations.

a) Name the products formed in each reaction.

b) Explain the difference in the reaction of the two alkali metals.

2

Reaction	Reactant 1	Reactant 2
X	Sodium	Iodine
Y	Bromine	Lithium
Z	Potassium	Chlorine

The table shows the reactants in three chemical reactions.

a) Name the products for each reaction.

b) Explain which reaction is likely to be the most violent.

3

A student cut a 2 cm³ cube of lithium. The surface inside was shiny.

She timed how long it took for the shiny surface to become dull.

a) Explain why the surface went dull.

b) Explain how the time would change if the experiment was repeated using sodium.

4   The flow chart shows some reactions of lithium. Name the substances A-D.

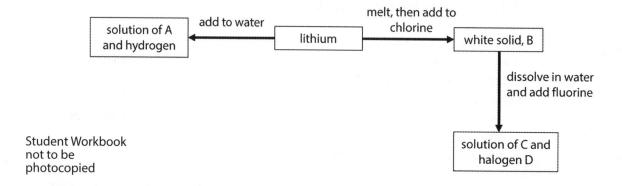

solution of A and hydrogen   ← add to water —   lithium   — melt, then add to chlorine →   white solid, B

white solid, B   — dissolve in water and add fluorine →   solution of C and halogen D

Example

5.1 Products of combustion

air hole open –
blue flame

air hole closed –
yellow flame

Jamie burns methane (CH_4) using a Bunsen burner. The flame is blue. He closes the air hole to turn the flame yellow. The glass boiling tube he is heating gets covered with a black powder.

Give an explanation for the observation.

 Detect

✓ **Values**

✓ **Unknown**

✓ **Concept**

I know that when the air hole is open, more air gets to the methane and the flame is blue. With the air hole closed, less air gets to the methane and the flame is yellow. I don't know why there is a yellow flame when there is less air or why heating with a yellow flame produces a black powder.

When methane burns, this is combustion. This question is about how the products of combustion change when the amount of air supplied to the fuel changes.

 Recall

What substances are produced when C and H combine with O_2?

1. **How atoms are oxidised in combustion.**

methane
CH_4

Methane is a hydrocarbon fuel. It contains only hydrogen and carbon atoms.
When fuels burn they react with oxygen.
When methane burns the carbon and hydrogen atoms combine with oxygen. They are oxidised.

2. **Why complete combustion happens with plenty of air.**

There is enough oxygen for each carbon atom to combine with two oxygen atoms.

methane + oxygen → carbon dioxide + water
CH_4 + $2O_2$ CO_2 + $2H_2O$

Carbon is fully oxidised to form carbon dioxide.

2. Why incomplete combustion happens with limited air.

Sometimes there is not enough oxygen for each carbon atom to combine with two oxygen atoms.

if there is very little oxygen ...   ... carbon is not oxidised.

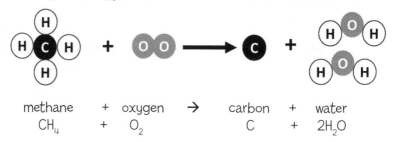

methane	+	oxygen	→	carbon	+	water
CH_4	+	O_2		C	+	$2H_2O$

if there is slightly more oxygen ...   ... carbon is partially oxidised to carbon monoxide.

3. How complete and incomplete combustion differ.

Product	Complete combustion	Incomplete combustion	What product looks like
Carbon dioxide (CO_2)	✓	✓	Colourless gas
Water (H_2O)	✓	✓	Colourless vapour or liquid
Carbon (C)	X	✓	Black solid (visible as smoke or soot)
Carbon monoxide (CO)	X	✓	Colourless gas, very toxic

 Solve

✅ Claim

✅ Evidence

✅ Reasoning

The black powder on the test tube is carbon, produced by incomplete combustion.
The black powder only appeared when the air hole was closed on the Bunsen burner.

Air hole open: methane reacts with plenty of oxygen in complete combustion. Each carbon atom reacts with two atoms of oxygen. Carbon is fully oxidised to produce carbon dioxide (colourless gas).

Air hole closed: the amount of oxygen reaching the methane is reduced. There is not enough oxygen for each carbon atom to combine with two oxygen atoms. Incomplete combustion produces carbon, the black solid.

Student Workbook
not to be
photocopied

1

A boiler uses methane gas to heat water to warm the house.
The flame should be regularly checked to make sure it is blue. A yellow flame means the boiler could be dangerous.
Explain why.

2

When the petrol in a vehicle engine burns, it releases the gases carbon monoxide, steam and sulfur dioxide.

From these observations, what elements do you think petrol contains? Explain your answer.

3

Electric motorbikes can use hydrogen (H_2) as a fuel.
a) Predict the product(s) of the complete combustion of hydrogen.
b) Hydrogen is often described as a 'cleaner' fuel than petrol. Explain why.

4

$$4CH_4 + 5O_2 \rightarrow 2\underline{\hspace{1cm}} + 2\underline{\hspace{1cm}} + 8\underline{\hspace{1cm}}$$

Incomplete combustion of hydrocarbons produces a mixture of products.
This is an equation for incomplete combustion of methane.
The products have been left blank.
Fill in the formulas of the products.

5.2 Calculate bond energies

A car manufacturer wants to use hydrogen as a car fuel.

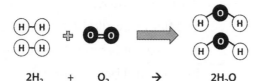

$2H_2 \quad + \quad O_2 \quad \rightarrow \quad 2H_2O$

The diagram shows how hydrogen reacts with oxygen.

Bond	Bond Energy (kJ/mol)
H-H	436
O=O	498
H-O	463

Use the bond energy data to explain if hydrogen could act as a fuel.

 Detect

✓ **Values**

The symbol equation shows me that two hydrogen molecules react with one oxygen molecule to form two water molecules.

The bond energies table tells me the amount of energy to break each chemical bond. For something to act as a fuel it needs to give out energy to its surroundings when it reacts.

✓ **Unknown**

I need to work out if hydrogen's reaction with oxygen releases energy or not.

✓ **Concept**

This question is about using bond energies to calculate energy changes in a reaction.

 Recall

1. How energy changes during a chemical reaction.

A chemical reaction involves energy changes. There are two stages:

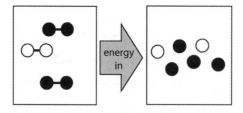

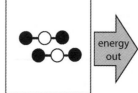

1. Energy is needed to break apart the bonds in the reactants.

2. Energy is released to the surroundings when new bonds form.

The energy taken and given out can be different.

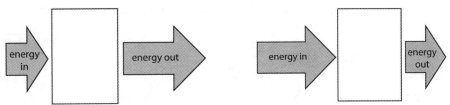

If the reaction gives out more energy than it takes in, there is a net release of energy.
This warms up the surroundings.
It is an exothermic reaction.

If the reaction takes in more energy than it gives out, the extra energy needed comes from the surroundings, So they cool down.
It is an endothermic reaction.

2. How to decide if a reaction is exothermic or endothermic.

A. Calculate energy in. Add the energies for the bonds that break (reactants on left of equation).

B. Calculate energy out. Add the energies for the bonds that form (products on right of equation).

C. Calculate: energy in - energy out.

D. If the answer is +ve, more energy is taken in by the system. It is endothermic. If the answer is -ve, more energy is given out by the system. It is exothermic.

> How do the diagrams explain this?

 Solve

A. Calculate energy in.
For the 2 H-H bonds. Breaking each bond takes in 436 kJ/mol.
So 2 x H-H = 2 × 436 = 872 kJ/mol.
For the O=O bond. Breaking each bond takes in 498 kJ/mol
Add the bond energies: 872 + 498 = 1370 kJ/mol

B. Calculate energy out.
For the 4 x O-H bonds. Making each bond gives out 463 kJ/mol.
So 4 × 463 = 1852 kJ/mol

C. Calculate energy in - energy out.
= 1370 - 1852 = - 482 kJ/mol

> Why is the sum this way round?

D. Is the energy change +ve or -ve?
The answer is negative. So it is an exothermic reaction.
The reaction of hydrogen with oxygen releases energy. So hydrogen could be used as a fuel in cars.

1 Carbon monoxide reacts with oxygen to make carbon dioxide.

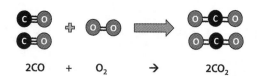

2CO + O₂ → 2CO₂

Bond	Bond Energy (kJ/mol)
O=O	498
H-O	463
C-H	413
C=O	799
C≡O	1072

Use the bond energy values to determine whether this reaction releases energy.

2

In a Bunsen burner, methane reacts with oxygen:

$$\text{H-}\overset{\displaystyle H}{\underset{\displaystyle H}{C}}\text{-H} + 2[O=O] \longrightarrow O=C=O + 2[H\text{-}O\text{-}H]$$

Explain why methane is a good choice for a Bunsen burner, using the bond energy data from Q1.

3

In a camping stove, propane reacts with oxygen. Work out the total bond energies of

A) The reactants

B) The products

Emma does this homework problem about a camping stove. Her answers are:

A) 5794 kJ/mol B) 4249 kJ/mol.

Emma's sister knew she had made a mistake just by looking at her answers.

Explain how her sister knew without adding bond energies.

4

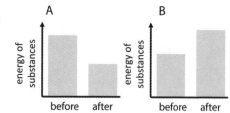

A   B

energy of substances

before   after   before   after

Hydrogen can be made by reacting methane with water:

$CH_4 + H_2O \longrightarrow 3H_2 + CO$

The energy needed to break the bonds in the reactants is 2578 kJ/mol.

The energy released when new bonds form in the products is 2380 kJ/mol.

a) Which bar chart shows the energy of the substances before and after the reaction? Explain your choice.

b) Suggest why this reaction has to be constantly heated.

1 /3 **2** /3 **3** /3 **4** /3 Total /12

5.3 Balance symbol equations

The gas ethene (C_2H_4) is bubbled through soapy water. When the bubbles are lit they burst into flames. The products of the reaction are carbon dioxide and steam.

Write out the balanced symbol equation for this reaction.

 Detect

✔ **Values**
✔ **Unknown**

I know ethene reacts to produce carbon dioxide and steam.

I need to write and balance the symbol equation.

 Recall

1. How a word equation shows the substances in a reaction.

Lighting ethene is a combustion reaction - ethene reacts with oxygen to release energy.

The word equation is: ethene + oxygen → water + carbon dioxide

2. How a symbol equation shows the number of atoms.

e.g. methane + oxygen → carbon dioxide + water

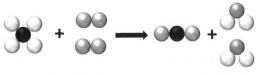

reactants (R)   products (P)

	R	P
⬤	1	1
◯	4	4
◯	4	4

Atoms are not be created or destroyed, so the numbers in each row should be the same.

The reactant atoms are rearranged to form products.

3. How to balance a symbol equation.

Put in the symbols for the ethene bubbles reaction:
$C_2H_4 + O_2 \rightarrow H_2O + CO_2$

	R	P
C	2	1
H	4	2
O	2	3

The numbers for each atom are different, so the equation is not balanced.

Why can't the small numbers be changed?

O_2 ⟨ $2O_2$ ✓ / O_4 ✗

To balance the atoms, you need to increase the amount of one or more substances by changing the numbers in front of them.

You cannot change the small numbers.

Recall

There are several methods to try to make the numbers balance.

Method A: Even up odd numbers.

$$C_2H_4 + O_2 \rightarrow H_2O + CO_2 \quad\Longrightarrow\quad C_2H_4 + O_2 \rightarrow \mathbf{2}H_2O + CO_2$$

make it **2**H_2O

	R	P
C	2	1
H	4	2
O	2	3

odd number of O atoms

H atoms now balance

	R	P
C	2	1
H	4	4
O	2	4

even number of O atoms (but they are not yet balanced)

Why are there 3 oxygen atoms in the products?

Method B: Double up when there is one atom.

$$C_2H_4 + O_2 \rightarrow H_2O + CO_2 \quad\Longrightarrow\quad C_2H_4 + O_2 \rightarrow \mathbf{2}H_2O + \mathbf{2}CO_2$$

make it **2**CO_2

	R	P
C	2	1
H	4	2
O	2	3

1 C atom

	R	P
C	2	2
H	4	2
O	2	4

the C atoms now balance, but the H atoms are not yet balanced

What would you do next?

Repeat these steps until the equation is balanced.

Solve

The symbol equation for the ethane reaction is:
$$C_2H_4 + O_2 \rightarrow H_2O + CO_2$$

Method A: Even up the odd numbers.
There are 3 O atoms in the products.

	R	P
C	2	1
H	4	4
O	2	4

$$C_2H_4 + O_2 \rightarrow \mathbf{2}H_2O + CO_2$$

The C and O atoms are not yet balanced.

Method B: Double up when there is one atom.
Turn the one C atom in the products into two by using $2CO_2$

	R	P
C	2	2
H	4	4
O	2	6

$$C_2H_4 + O_2 \rightarrow \mathbf{2}H_2O + \mathbf{2}CO_2$$

The O atoms are still not balanced.

Balance the O atoms by tripling the O_2.

	R	P
C	2	2
H	4	4
O	6	6

$$C_2H_4 + \mathbf{3}O_2 \rightarrow \mathbf{2}H_2O + \mathbf{2}CO_2$$

Now all the numbers of atoms are equal so the equation is balanced.

Your turn

1

Farmers use fertilisers to improve plant growth. They are made from ammonia (NH_3).

The ammonia is generated from the Haber process where hydrogen gas (H_2) reacts with nitrogen gas (N_2).

Write the balanced symbol equation for the Haber process.

2

sodium hydroxide solution NaOH

copper sulfate solution $CuSO_4$

solid copper hydroxide $Cu(OH)_2$ in sodium sulfate solution Na_2SO_4

The diagram shows copper sulfate reacting with sodium hydroxide.

Write a balanced symbol equation for the reaction.

3

Substance		Number of particles
Reactants	Iron oxide	1
	Carbon monoxide	3
Products	Iron	2
	Carbon dioxide	3

Iron is found in the earth as the compound iron oxide.

To make pure iron, the iron oxide is heated with carbon monoxide (CO) in a blast furnace. The table shows the number of particles of each substance in the reaction.
What is the formula of the iron oxide?

4

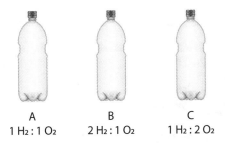

A
$1 H_2 : 1 O_2$

B
$2 H_2 : 1 O_2$

C
$1 H_2 : 2 O_2$

Hydrogen can explode when mixed with oxygen, producing water. The biggest explosion occurs when the reactants are present in exactly the right amounts, leaving nothing unreacted. A teacher put different ratios of hydrogen and oxygen into a bottle and set light to them.
Which bottle had the biggest explosion? Explain your choice.

5.4 Calculate mass with equations

A scientist heats a 4.8 g piece of magnesium in air until all the magnesium is reacted.

The symbol equation is:

$2Mg + O_2 \rightarrow 2MgO$

Calculate the mass of oxygen that was used in the reaction.

Relative atomic masses (A_r): Mg=24, O=16

 Detect

✓ **Values**

I know the relative atomic masses of the atoms involved in the reaction.

I know that 4.8 g of magnesium reacts. The equation tells me it reacts with oxygen to produce magnesium oxide. It also tells me the number of atoms of each reactant and product.

✓ **Unknown**

✓ **Concept**

I don't know the mass of oxygen or magnesium oxide.

This question is about using equations to calculate mass.

Recall

1. How the equation shows relative numbers of particles in a reaction.

$$2Mg + O_2 \rightarrow 2MgO$$

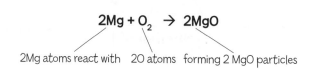

2Mg atoms react with   2O atoms   forming 2 MgO particles

> How does the equation tell me that 2 oxygen atoms react?

2. How a chemical reaction rearranges atoms.

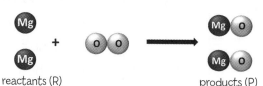

reactants (R)   products (P)

	R	P
Mg	2	2
O	2	2

The number of atoms of each element is the same on both sides (atoms can't be created or destroyed).

3. How mass is conserved in a reaction.

The mass of the products after a reaction must be the same as the mass of reactants before the reaction.

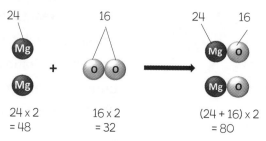

24   16   24   16

24 x 2   16 x 2   (24 + 16) x 2
= 48   = 32   = 80

Calculate the mass of each particle (formula mass) then add them together

Total formula mass = 80 (48 + 32)   Total formula mass = 80

4. How to calculate masses of reactants and products.

Now I can work out unknown masses.

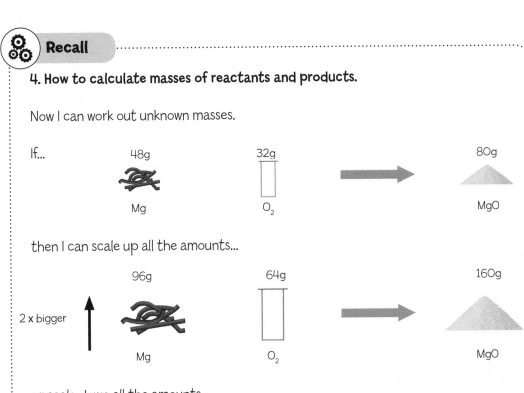

If...

| 48g | 32g | | 80g |
| Mg | O_2 | → | MgO |

then I can scale up all the amounts...

2 x bigger

| 96g | 64g | | 160g |
| Mg | O_2 | → | MgO |

or scale down all the amounts...

2 x smaller

| 24g | 16g | | 40g |
| Mg | O_2 | → | MgO |

Solve

The question says that 4.8 g of magnesium reacts.

I need to work out the mass of oxygen that reacts with this much magnesium.

Because the number of atoms are conserved in a reaction:

total formula mass of reactants = total formula mass of products

$$2Mg + O_2 \rightarrow 2MgO$$
$$48 + 32 = 80$$

i.e. 48 g magnesium reacts with 32 g oxygen to form 80 g magnesium oxide.

But the question asks about 4.8g - only 1/10th as much.

So I scale down all the numbers by a factor of 10.

i.e. 4.8 g magnesium reacts with 3.2 g oxygen to form 8.0 g magnesium oxide.

1

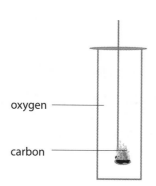

oxygen

carbon

A scientist burns a 1.2 g piece of carbon in a gas jar of oxygen.

The symbol equation for the reaction is:
$C + O_2 \rightarrow CO_2$

What mass of oxygen is needed for the carbon to completely react?
Relative atomic masses (A_r): C=12, O=16.

2

| iron + carbon | $\rightarrow$ | iron + carbon |
| oxide monoxide | | dioxide |

$Fe_2O_3 + \quad 3CO \quad \rightarrow \quad 2Fe + 3CO_2$

Iron is extracted from iron oxide by reacting it with carbon monoxide.
How much iron oxide is needed to make 224 g of iron?
Relative atomic masses (A_r): Fe=56, O=16, C=12

3

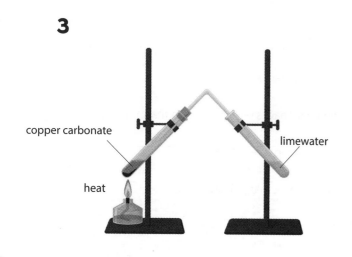

copper carbonate

limewater

heat

A student heats 1.235 g of copper carbonate to make it decompose.
The equation for the reaction is:
$CuCO_3 \rightarrow CuO + CO_2$
The carbon dioxide is bubbled through limewater. It all reacts with the limewater to form a solid precipitate.
Calculate the increase in mass of the limewater.
Relative atomic masses (A_r): Cu=63.5, C=12, O=16

4

iron + sulfur $\rightarrow$ iron sulfide

$Fe + \quad S \quad \rightarrow \quad FeS$

A teacher heats 6 g of iron filings with 3.2 g of sulfur powder.
They react to form iron sulfide.
Calculate how much iron is left unreacted.
Relative atomic masses (A_r): Fe = 56, S=32

| **1** | /3 | **2** | /3 | **3** | /3 | **4** | /3 | Total | /12 | © Mastery Science 2018 |

6.1 Reactivity series

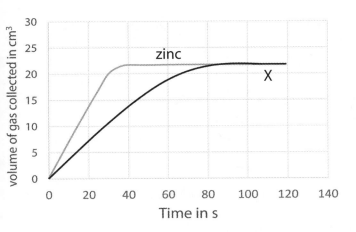

Phoebe is given an unknown metal powder, X. She knows it is either copper, iron or magnesium. To find out which, she adds 25 cm³ of dilute hydrochloric acid to X. She also adds the same volume of acid to the same mass of zinc.
She measures how the volume of gas produced by each reaction changes over 2 minutes.

Name metal X. Give a reason for your answer.

 Detect

✓ **Values**

The graph shows that both metals produced 25 cm³ of gas. It took zinc 40 seconds and X 100 seconds. Phoebe used the same volume of liquid, mass of metal and both metals were powdered so none of these variables could explain the difference.

✓ **Unknown**

I need to work out what metal X is by comparing it to zinc.

✓ **Concept**

The question is about the reactivity of metals.

 Recall

1. **How metals react with different substances.**

Reaction with	Example
Oxygen	magnesium + oxygen magnesium oxide
Water	sodium + water sodium hydroxide + hydrogen
Acid	calcium + hydrochloric acid calcium chloride + hydrogen

2. **How the reactivity of different metals varies.**

Reaction with water

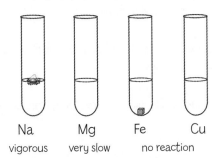

Na	Mg	Fe	Cu
vigorous	very slow	no reaction	

Reaction with dilute acids

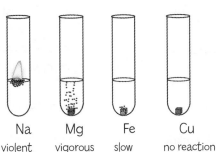

Na	Mg	Fe	Cu
violent	vigorous	slow	no reaction

Which metal is the most reactive?

A metal that produces more vigorous changes is called a more reactive metal.

3. How ions relate to reactivity.

> Why do magnesium ions have a +2 charge?

When metals react, they lose the electrons in their outer shell and form positive ions.

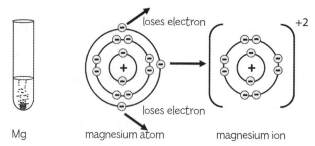

Mg   magnesium atom   magnesium ion

The more easily a metal forms a positive ion, the more reactive it is.

4. How a reactivity series predicts a metal's reactions.

A reactivity series puts metals in order of reactivity.

> Are all metals shown in this reactivity series?

most reactive

K	potassium
Na	sodium
Li	lithium
Ca	calcium
Mg	magnesium
Al	aluminium
Zn	zinc
Fe	iron
Cu	copper

least reactive

reacts with water

reacts with dilute acids

reacts with oxygen

Knowing a metal's position tells you how vigorously it reacts.

💡 **Solve**

✓ **Claim**

X is iron.

✓ **Evidence**

The graph shows that it took X 100 seconds to produce all the hydrogen gas, whereas zinc took 40 seconds.

✓ **Reasoning**

Therefore X produces hydrogen more slowly than zinc. As its reaction is less vigorous, X must be a less reactive metal than zinc.

✓ **Evidence**

The reactivity series shows metals in order of reactivity. It shows two metals that are less reactive than zinc: iron and copper.

✓ **Reasoning**

However, copper does not react with dilute acids. Only iron does, so X must be iron.

1

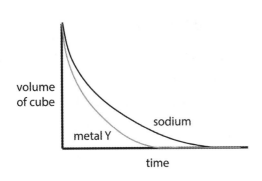

Asif added a cube of sodium to water. He measured the volume of the cube until it had all reacted.

He repeated the experiment with an unknown metal, Y, using a cube of the same size. The graph shows the results.

Suggest what metal Y is. Give a reason.

2

Nickel is between iron and copper in the reactivity series.

Dana adds a piece of nickel to a colourless liquid at room temperature. She observes bubbles.

Is the liquid likely to be water or acid? Explain your choice.

3

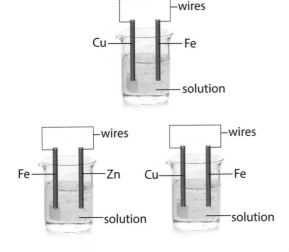

In a battery cell, two metals are connected by a wire and a solution that conducts electricity.

A current flows because the more reactive metal loses electrons which flow through the solution to the less reactive metal. The bigger the difference in the reactivity of the metals, the bigger the current.

a) Predict the direction that the electrons flow for A, B and C.

b) Which cell has the biggest current? Explain your choice.

4

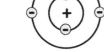

lithium   beryllium

The diagram shows atoms of lithium and beryllium. Lithium reacts readily with cold water. Beryllium reacts with steam, but not with cold water.

Suggest why lithium is more reactive than beryllium.

6.2 Displacement reactions

Callum added unknown metals A, B, C and D to different salt solutions .

Results

3 combinations showed a reaction:

Metal C + salt solution of metal A

Metal D + salt solution of metal B

Metal A + salt solution of metal D

a) Callum thinks B could be sodium. Explain why this is unlikely.

b) Predict whether metal D and a salt solution of metal A will react. Give a reason.

 Detect

✓ Diagram

✓ Values

✓ Unknown

✓ Concept

A table shows which metals react with which salts (✓ = reaction).

I do not know the names of the metals A-D.
This question is about reactivity of metals and displacement reactions.

Metal	Metal salt solution			
	A	B	C	D
A				✓
B				
C	✓			
D		✓		

 Recall

1. How a salt is made of metal and non-metal.

sodium   chloride

metal   non-metal

A salt is a compound.
The name shows its elements.

2. How to think of displacement reactions.

Displacement is a bit like bullying - metals do what people shouldn't, they snatch things from others. Displacement is a more reactive metal snatching the non-metal from a less reactive one.

Imagine the small boy is the unreactive metal (D). The football is the non-metal, and boy + football is the salt.

The big bad bully is the more reactive metal (B).

Before

After

 **+**  →

The unreactive metal is in a salt

The reactive metal is not

Now the reactive metal is in a salt

The unreactive metal is not

Why is there no reaction, in terms of boys & footballs?

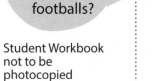 **+** →  **+**

When the more reactive metal is in a salt, there is no reaction.

3. How a reactivity series predicts a metal's reactions.

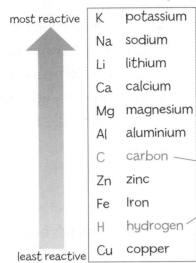

The metals can be ordered into a series. with the more reactive metals near the top.

A metal higher in a series displaces a metal lower in a series from its salt.

Carbon and hydrogen are not metals but they are often placed in a reactivity series because they are used to extract metals from their ores using displacement reactions.

 Solve

✓ Claim

✓ Evidence

a) Metal B is unlikely to be sodium because it is the least reactive of the four metal.s In displacement reactions, a more reactive metal displaces a less reactive one from its compound.

Metal	Salt			
	A	B	C	D
B				

Metal B did not react with any other metal salts.

✓ Evidence
✓ Reasoning

Metal	Salt
	B
D	✓

Metal D displaces B which means B is less reactive than D.

✓ Evidence
✓ Reasoning

Metal	Salt
	D
A	✓

D is less reactive than A.

✓ Evidence
✓ Reasoning

Metal	Salt
	A
C	✓

A is less reactive than C.

B is the least reactive metal. We know sodium is reactive so B is unlikely to be sodium.

✓ Claim

✓ Evidence

✓ Reasoning

most reactive

C
A
D
B

least reactive

b) I predict that there will be no reaction between metal D and a metal A salt.

I can construct a reactivity series. I can see metal D is is less reactive than metal A.
So metal D cannot displace metal A from its salt.
Therefore there is no reaction.

Your turn

1 Penny carried out some reactions by adding metals W, X, Y and Z to solutions of their salts.

Results

Metal Y did not react with any solution.

3 combinations showed a reaction:

Metal X + salt solution of W

Metal X + salt solution of Y

Metal Z + salt solution of W.

a) Penny thinks that metal Y could be copper. Explain why this is likely.

b) Can the information predict if there is a reaction between metal X and a salt solution of metal Z? Give a reason for your answer.

2

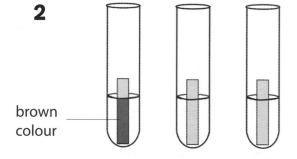

brown colour

bismuth   tungsten   silver

Copper is a brown-coloured metal.

Zac added the metals bismuth, tungsten and silver to copper sulfate solution.

He observed that the bismuth went brown but tungsten and silver did not.

a) Give an explanation for the observations.

b) Describe what Zac needs to do to place the metals in order of reactivity.

3

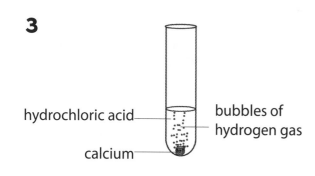

hydrochloric acid

calcium

bubbles of hydrogen gas

When calcium is added to dilute hydrochloric acid the following reaction takes place:

$Ca + 2HCl \rightarrow CaCl_2 + H_2$

a) Explain why this reaction happens.

b) Explain why iron reacts with dilute hydrochloric acid, but gold does not.

4

Most metals are not found pure in the ground but combined with other elements in compounds called ores.

A rock contains a mixture of metal ores: aluminium oxide, copper sulfide, iron oxide and magnesium carbonate.

A scientist heated the rock with carbon in a furnace.

Explain what metals would be produced.

Student Workbook not to be photocopied

6.3 Making potable water

A water company plans to use river water to supply a town with potable water.

	Potable water	River water
Cloudiness	<4	17
Sodium chloride	<200 mg/dm^3	35 mg/dm^3
Harmful bacteria	0 per 100 cm^3	505 per 100 cm^3
pH	6.5-8.5	6.3

The table shows how the river water compares with potable water.

Use the results in the table to explain how to make the river water safe to drink.

 Detect

✓ **Values**

The data shows that some substances in the river water are above the limits for potable water. The cloudiness and number of harmful bacteria are too high. The pH is too low.

✓ **Unknown**

I need to identify methods to solve these problems with the river water.

✓ **Concept**

This question is about methods for producing potable water.

 Recall

1. How to remove insoluble substances.

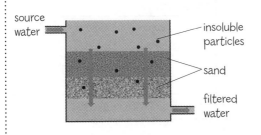

The water is cloudy because of particles that do not dissolve in water. Filtering removes insoluble substances. It is done using filter beds.

As the water flows through the sand, the particles come close to sand grains and stick to them.

Filtering removes some but not all microorganisms.

2. How to remove dissolved substances.

There are two methods, distillation and reverse osmosis. As they both remove salt, they are referred to as desalination. Both use a lot of energy, so are expensive.

A. Distillation

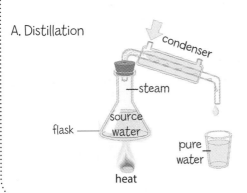

The source water is heated and boils to form steam.
The steam condenses back to liquid water in the condenser.
The water collected in the beaker is pure - it contains no other substances.
The dissolved substances are left behind in the flask.
Distillation also removes insoluble substances and microorganisms.

Why is distilled water potable?

B. Reverse osmosis.

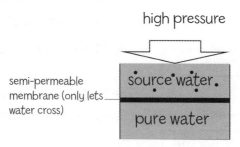

high pressure

semi-permeable membrane (only lets water cross)

source water

pure water

Normal osmosis would not purify the source water. Here the water has to move from high solute concentration to low (and osmosis means the opposite).

So to reverse the process of osmosis, high pressure is used. It forces the water to move across the membrane. Reverse osmosis also removes insoluble substances and microorganisms, which do not move through the membrane.

3. How to remove microorganisms.

Distillation or reverse osmosis will remove microorganisms.

Other methods to kill microorganisms (sterilisation) are:

- Bubbling chlorine or ozone through the water
- Shining UV light on the water

4. How to adjust the pH

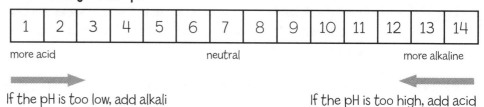

| 1 | 2 | 3 | 4 | 5 | 6 | 7 | 8 | 9 | 10 | 11 | 12 | 13 | 14 |

more acid   neutral   more alkaline

If the pH is too low, add alkali   If the pH is too high, add acid

 Solve

I can reorganise the to identify the problems with the river water.

Problem	Solution
Cloudiness: too high	Filter using filter beds. Insoluble particles get stuck to sand grains
Harmful bacteria: too high	Add chlorine/ozone/UV light to kill microorganisms
pH: too low	Add alkali to increase pH

The water company can use these methods to make the water potable:

1. Cloudiness too high
Use filter beds remove small insoluble particles. They contain layers of sand. The river water flows through the sand and the insoluble particles become stuck to the sand grains.

✓ Problem
✓ Solution

2 Harmful bacteria too high
Use sterilisation. Bubble chlorine or ozone through the water or shine UV light on it. This kills the bacteria in the water.

✓ Problem
✓ Solution

3. pH too low
Add alkali to increase the pH so it between 6.5 and 8.5.

Your turn

1

	Potable water	Sea water
Cloudiness	<4	3
Sodium chloride	<200 mg/dm³	10 205 MG/DM³
Harmful bacteria	0 per 100 cm³	341 per 100 cm³
pH	6.5-8.5	8.7

A country is planning to use seawater as a source of potable water.

The table shows how the sea water compares with potable water

Use the results in the table to explain how to make the sea water safe to drink.

2

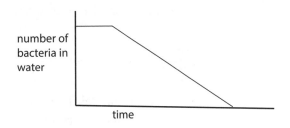

The diagram shows the stages of water treatment.
The graph shows a change in the water. At which location (A-E) would you see this change? Give a reason for your choice.

3

	Potable water	Source X	Source Y
Sodium chloride	<200 mg/dm³	24 mg/dm³	12 000 mg/dm3
Harmful bacteria	0 per 100 cm³	1500 per 100 cm³	13 per 100 cm3
pH	6.5-8.5	6.6	7.1

An island needs to increase their potable water supply. They only have a small budget. They test the water from two different sources – X and Y. Both sources can be treated to make potable water. Which source would you recommend? Give reasons for your choice.

4

Pasha is asked to test a sample of water to find out the mass of any dissolved substances.

Describe how he can use the equipment shown to find out.

 **Example**

6.4 Environmental impact

Factor	Disposable	Reusable
Material	Plastic (finite, not biodegradable)	Cotton (renewable, biodegradable)
Energy to make it (kWh)	338	57
Water to make it (dm3)	10500	1500
Lifetime (number of uses)	1	167
Lifetime energy to wash it (kWh)	0	141

A mother-to-be is considering which type of nappy to buy for her baby: disposable or reusable.

Use the data and your knowledge to compare the environmental impact of each nappy during its life cycle.

Detect

The table shows the data about two types of nappies.
I need to use the data to compare these impacts of each type of nappy.
This question is about the concept of using resources and the skill of analysing the environmental impact of a product.

- ✓ Values
- ✓ Unknown
- ✓ Concept

Recall

1. How to model the environmental impact of a product.

Products require raw materials and manufacturing, and then are used and disposed of. These stages make up a product's life cycle. At each stage, the product has some impact on the environment.

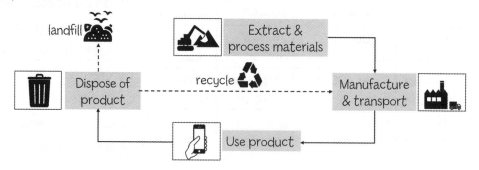

2. How to compare the data.

You can only compare numbers if there are measuring the same thing.

Factor	Disposable	Reusable
Energy to make it (kWh)	338	57
Lifetime (number of uses)	1	167

Unfair comparison: The data show that reusable nappies last 167 times as long as a disposable.

Factor	Disposable	Reusable
Energy to make 167 nappies (kWh)	56 446	57

Fair comparison: I need to calculate the energy for 167 disposables nappies = 338 x 167 and then compare.

Student Workbook not to be photocopied

3. How to assess the impact of the product.

Each stage has inputs (e.g. resources) and creates outputs (e.g. polluting gases). Both affect the environment.

What other impacts are there?

Stage	Impacts		
	Input: resources	Input: energy	Output: ecosystems
Extract & process	Are raw materials finite or renewable?	How much electricity is used?	Are habitats destroyed?
Manufacture & transport	How much water is used? What is the packaging?	How much fuel is used during transport?	How much pollution is released? How far must the product travel?
Use product	Does it need cleaning?	How-energy efficient is it?	Does it release pollution?
Dispose product	Can it be reused or recycled?	How much energy does recycling take?	Is it biodegradable?

4. How to consider other information.

Some of the outputs may not have been measured. If no numbers are given, you have to make a judgement.

Sometimes companies show or hide information to make the product more appealing.

 Solve

I have analysed the 4 stages of a product's lifecycle, using the information given.

Stage	Impacts	Better?
Extract & process	Reusable: cotton is renewable Disposable: plastics are finite	Reusables
Manufacture & transport	Reusable: It takes 57 kWh and 1050 dm^3 of water to make one reusable Disposable: Because 167 disposables are needed for every reusable, it takes 56 446 kWh and 1 753 500 dm^3 of water to make the disposable nappies	Reusables
Use product	Reusable: have to be washed Disposable: no energy is needed	Disposables
Dispose product	Reusable: can be used many times, and the material is biodegradable Disposable: are used once. They are not biodegradable, and may release toxic chemicals in landfill.	Reusables

Overall, reusable nappies have a smaller environmental impact.

1

Factor	Glass bottle	Plastic bottle
Raw materials	Sand, limestone, salt	Crude oil
Mass (g)	350	25
Maximum temperature in production process (°C)	1600	850
How many times is the bottle used?	24	1
% recycled at end of life	35	5

A milk delivery company is thinking of switching from glass to plastic milk bottles.

Use the data in the table and your knowledge to compare the environmental impact of each bottle during its life cycle.

2

About 70% of plastic bottles used in UK households are disposed of in landfill sites. On average they are transported 50 km.
The other 30% of bottles are sent 20 000 km to Asia for recycling.

Assess the environmental impact of each disposal method.

3

Every year, Ali buys the latest model of his mobile phone.
Cherie says he can reduce his environmental impact by only changing his phone every two years.
Give one piece of evidence for and against Cherie's claim.

4

Factor	Ceramic cup	Paper cup
Raw materials	Clay (renewable)	Trees (renewable) Plastic liner (finite)
Mass (g)	250	5
Water used in manufacture (dm3)	650	4500
Mass of CO2 produced during manufacture (kg)	0.3	2.2
Disposal	Reused	88% sent to landfill 12% incinerated (burnt)

A manufacturer claims its reusable ceramic coffee cups have less impact on the environment than paper cups.
a) Use this information taken from on the website to assess the claim.
b) Why might this information not be completely accurate?

7.1 Cell magnification

plant cell

bacterial cell

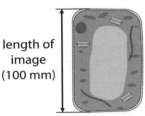

length of image
(100 mm)

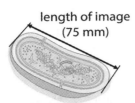

length of image
(75 mm)

magnification:
X2000

magnification:
X15 000

The images show two cells at different magnifications.

a) Calculate the length of each cell in μm.

b) Give the order of magnitude difference in the lengths of the cells.

You can use the equation:

$$\text{magnification} = \frac{\text{image size}}{\text{object size}}$$

 Detect

✓ Values
✓ Unknown
✓ Concept

I know the magnification and the lengths of the images, in mm.
I need to calculate the object size, the real length of the cells, in μm.
This question is about magnification, changing the subject of an equation and converting units.

 Recall

What version of the formula will I need to use?

1. How magnification is a ratio of image : object size.
Magnification means how many times larger an image is than the real object.

$$\text{magnification} = \frac{\text{image size}}{\text{object size}} \quad \text{It is a ratio of these two quantities.}$$

2 mm

X20
magnification

real object

40 mm

image

$$\text{magnification} \quad = \frac{40}{2} = X20$$

2. How to convert units and use powers of 10.

each prefix is
1000 x smaller

÷1000

milli- and micro-
show fractions of a
metre

Prefix	In metres	Power of ten
k (kilo)	1000 m	10^3
–	1 m	10^0
m (milli)	1/1 000th m	10^{-3}
μ (micro)	1/100 0000th m	10^{-6}
n (nano)	1/100 000 000th m	10^{-9}

10 to the power 3 means x10 x10 x10

10 to the power -6 means
÷10 ÷10 ÷10
÷10 ÷10 ÷10
10^{-6} is easier to write

3. How to work out orders of magnitude.
Order of magnitude means the number of powers of 10 in a number.
10^3 The order of magnitude is 3.
10^{-3} The order of magnitude is –3.

Recall

3. How to find object size from image size..

Method A: Use magnification ratio.

60mm

| image | ÷20 magnification | ? real object |

I want to find the object size.
If the magnification is X20, the image is 20 times bigger than the real object.
To find the object size, I divide the image size by 20.
Size of real object = $\frac{60}{20}$ = 3 mm.

Method B: Rearrange the equation.

To get image size on its own, multiply both sides by object size.

magnification = $\frac{\text{image size}}{\text{object size}}$

x object size   x object size

→ magnification x object size = image size

To get object size on its own, divide both sides by magnification.

magnification x object size = image size

÷ magnification   ÷ magnification

→ object size = $\frac{\text{image size}}{\text{magnification}}$

> Which method do you think is easiest?

Solve

a) I know the magnification and image length. I need to find the object length.

Method A: Use magnification ratio
The plant cell image has a magnification of X2000. So, the real object is 2000 times smaller than the image.
Object length for plant cell = 100/2000 = 0.05 mm

Method B: Use the equation:
I can write the magnification equation is this form:

object size = $\frac{\text{image size}}{\text{magnification}}$

Now I can substitute the numbers.
Object size for bacterial cell = 90/15 000 = 0.006 mm

Then I convert mm to μm
Plant cell = 0.05 x 1000 = 50 μm
Bacterial cell = 0.006 x 1000 = 6 μm

> How does standard form make differences in orders of magnitude clear?

b) Calculate difference in orders of magnitude:
Plant cell = 50 μm = 50/1 000 000 = 0.00005 m = 5×10^{-5} m.
Its order of magnitude is -5.
Bacterial cell = 6 μm = 6/1 000 000 = 0.000006 m = 6×10^{-6} m
Its order of magnitude is -6. There is one order of magnitude difference in the lengths of the cells.

Your turn

1

measles virus

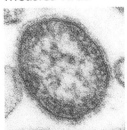

magnification:
X450 000

white blood cell

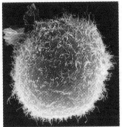

magnification:
X2500

A student looks at images from an electron microscope, taken at different magnifications.

He measures the diameter of each cell as 55 mm.
a) Calculate the real length of each cell in μm.
b) Give the order of magnitude difference in the lengths of the cells.
You can use the equation:

$$\text{magnification} = \frac{\text{image size}}{\text{object size}}$$

2

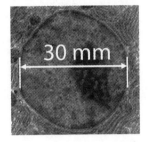

30 mm

This image is of a cell nucleus.
The real diameter of the nucleus is 6×10^{-3} mm.
Calculate the magnification of the image.

3

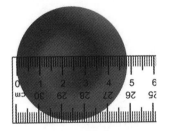

A student used a ruler to measure the diameter of a blood cell image.
Calculate the number of orders of magnitude difference in the image and the real cell.

4

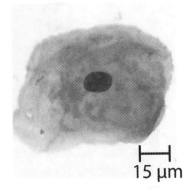

15 μm

The image shows a cheek cell.
Samira says the diameter of the cell is 4 orders of magnitude bigger than the diameter of the nucleus.
She is wrong. Explain what the correct answer is.

7.2 Cell division changes

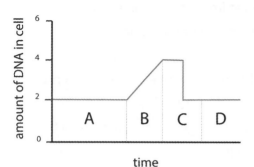

The graph shows how the amount of DNA in a cell changes as it goes through the cell cycle.

Explain what happens during sections B and C and why these are important for the cell.

Detect

- ✓ **Values**
- ✓ **Unknown**
- ✓ **Concept**

The graph shows that in section B the amount of DNA doubles. In section C it halves again suddenly.

I need to explain why the amount of DNA changes and what is happening to the cell. This is a question about cell division.

Recall

> What happens during the cell cycle?

1. How cell division is important for the body.

Humans constantly need to make new cells to grow and repair damage. This happens by cells dividing – each cell becomes two identical daughter cells.

Cell go through a cycle of stages.

cells divide in this stage

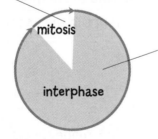

mitosis

in this stage, cells carry out their normal role and prepare for division

interphase

2. How the cell prepares for division during interphase.

First, the cell grows.

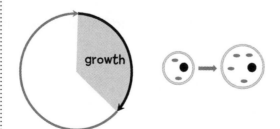

growth

The size of the cell increases. The amount of cytoplasm and number of cell structures like mitochondria doubles.

Recall

Next, the cell copies its genetic material.

single chromosomes

chromosome copies

Each strand of DNA is copied to form two copies of each chromosome. There is now one copy of each chromosome for the daughter cells.

DNA replication

After replication, there is another stage of growth, and the cell is ready to divide.

more growth

Why do the daughter cells contain the same amount of DNA as the parent cell?

3. How mitosis works.
The chromosome copies are split apart during mitosis.

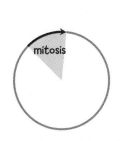

mitosis

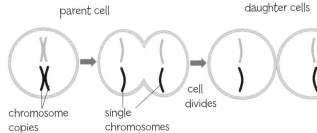

parent cell

daughter cells

chromosome copies

single chromosomes

cell divides

 Solve

✓ Claim

✓ Evidence

✓ Reasoning

✓ Claim

✓ Evidence

✓ Reasoning

Section B
This shows the stage in the cell cycle where it replicates its DNA.
In section B, the amount of DNA doubles.
The cell must be making another copy of each chromosome.
This stage is important because the cell needs two copies so it can pass one to each daughter cell.

Section C
This shows the stage in the cell cycle called mitosis.
In section C, the amount of DNA in each cell halves.
This must be when the parent cell divides to form two daughter cells. The chromosome copies are split so each daughter cells receives one copy, the same number as the parent cell. This stage is important because cell division makes new cells and is important for growth and repair.

1

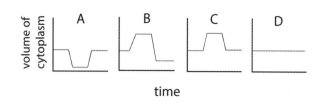

A single cell goes through one cell cycle. Which graph shows the correct changes in the volume of cytoplasm in the cell? Explain your answer.

2

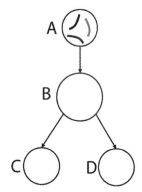

The diagram shows cell A undergoing the cell cycle.

Three chromosomes are shown in cell A.

Copy and complete the diagram to show the chromosomes in cells B, C and D.

3

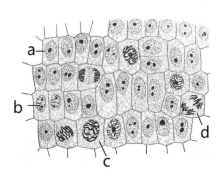

A scientist viewed onion cells under a microscope.

Cell a is not dividing.

Cells b, c and d show cells at one of the three stages in the cell cycle.

She counted the number of cells of each type:

a	b	c	d
20	3	5	1

Which stage is fastest in the cell cycle?

Give a reason for your answer.

4

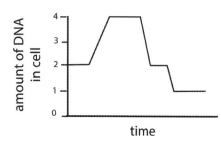

Cells in a man's testes divide to produce sperm cells.

The graph shows how the amount of DNA changes during this process.

a) Explain if the testes cells divide by mitosis.

b) The cells in the testes contain 46 chromosomes. Use the graph to predict the number of chromosomes in the sperm cells.

1 /3 **2** /3 **3** /3 **4** /3 Total /12 © Mastery Science 2018

7.3 Types of cell transport

Plants need minerals A,B and C for healthy growth. The table shows the concentration of these minerals in plant root cells and in the surrounding soil in normal conditions.

Mineral	Concentration in plant root cells in mol/dm³	Concentration in surrounding soil in mol/dm³
A	0.7	0.5
B	0.2	0.4
C	0.8	1.0

Heavy rain can leave the soil waterlogged, which decreases oxygen reaching the root cells.

For which mineral will the movement into the cells be reduced?

Explain your choice.

 Detect

✓ Values

✓ Unknown

✓ Concept

The question says that minerals must move from the soil into the root cells. The table shows that the concentrations inside the cells and in the soil are different.

I need to work out which mineral is affected by a lack of oxygen.

The question is about cell transport and what affects it.

 Recall

Why does diffusion happen?

1. How substances move in/out of cells by diffusion.

Particles in a solution are constantly moving. When there is a higher concentration of a substance on one side of a cell membrane...

...more particles will move across the membrane in this direction.

...and a smaller number move this way.

There is a net movement in this direction.
Diffusion is the movement of a substances from high to low concentration, or 'down the concentration gradient'. It happens without using the cell's energy.

2. How substances move in/out of cells by active transport.

There is a higher concentration of particles inside. Therefore diffusion will not move this substance into the cell.

The cell uses active transport instead.

How does active transport happen?

a protein in the membrane helps the substance across

but it takes energy to flip the protein

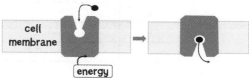

Active transport uses energy to move substances across cell membranes from low to high concentration, or against the concentration gradient.

3. How substances get their energy from respiration.

How does a lack of oxygen affect cell transport?

	Aerobic	Anaerobic
Reactants	Glucose and oxygen	Just glucose
Energy produced	A large amount	A small amount

Cells need energy for life processes. They get it from breaking down glucose using either aerobic or anaerobic respiration.

 Solve

✓ **Claim**

✓ **Evidence**
✓ **Reasoning**

Mineral A: its movement will be affected by a reduction in oxygen.

The concentration of A inside the root cells is higher than the soil.
So it cannot move in by diffusion, but must move by active transport.
Active transport require energy which comes from respiration. Aerobic respiration provides the most energy but requires oxygen.
If the cell receives less oxygen, it will start switch to anaerobic respiration, which produces less energy. So the active transport of A is reduced.

✓ **Claim**

✓ **Evidence**

✓ **Reasoning**

Minerals B & C: Their movement will not be affected.

The concentration of B & C inside the root cells is lower than the soil.
So they can move in by diffusion.
Diffusion does not require energy from the cell. So the movement of B & C will not be affected by the cell switching from aerobic to anaerobic respiration.

1

Mineral	Concentration in mmol/dm³	
	Outside cells	Inside cells
Calcium	120	5
Chloride	3	28
Potassium	6	135
Sodium	139	11

Scientists studied the movement of minerals that normally flow into human cells.

They measured the initial concentrations of ions outside and inside the cells.

Then they added cyanide, a poison that stops respiration.

Explain the effect of stopping respiration on the movement of each mineral.

2

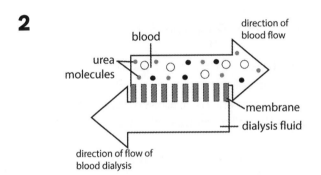

In kidney disease urea builds up in the blood. The diagram shows how a treatment works.

Explain how a moving stream of dialysis fluid can help the patient.

3

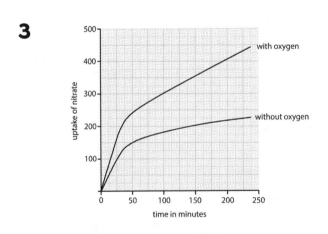

A student does an experiment to find out whether nitrates are absorbed by plants using diffusion or active transport.

Which method(s) of absorption does the data support? Explain your choice.

4

	Relative rate of absorption	
Sugar	Normal intestine	Intestine poisoned by cyanide
Glucose	10.1	3.45
Xylose	3.02	3.04

Scientists measured how quickly the cells in a piece of normal intestine absorbed two different sugars. They repeated the experiment after poisoning the intestine with cyanide, which stops respiration.

Use the data from the table to explain which sugar(s) are absorbed by:

a) Active transport

b) Diffusion.

7.4 Predict diffusion

Cell	Concentration of oxygen in mg/l	
	Outside cell	Inside cell
A	10.3	7.3
B	2.0	91.2
C	7.4	7.4
D	5.4	2.2

The mitochondria in cells need oxygen to carry out aerobic respiration.
A scientist measured the oxygen levels inside and outside four similar size cells at the start of an experiment.

In which cell will oxygen move fastest across the cell membrane? Give a reason for your choice.

Detect

✓ Diagram

✓ Values

✓ Unknown

✓ Concept

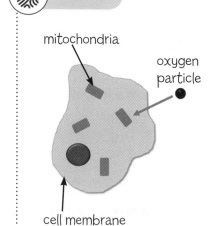

mitochondria

oxygen particle

cell membrane

Mitochondria are found inside cells.

The table shows that the concentrations of oxygen inside and outside each cell are different.
I need to find which cell allows oxygen to move across the cell membrane into the cell fastest.

The question is about cell transport, how substances move into and out of cells.

Recall

How can diffusion be explained using particles?

1. How oxygen moves into cells by diffusion.

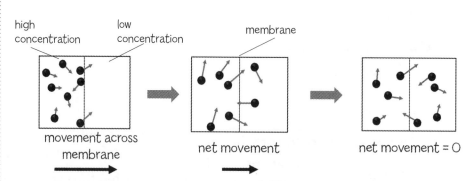

high concentration   low concentration   membrane

movement across membrane

all particles are on the left, so they cross quickly

net movement

more particles are on the left, but now some are on the right so the net movement is slower

net movement = 0

same number of particles on each side, so they cross in both directions equally

Diffusion is the movement of a substance from an area of high to low concentration. It happens with or without a membrane.

What affects the rate of diffusion?

3. How temperature affects the speed of diffusion.

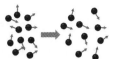

low temperature: particles spread slower

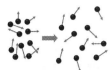

high temperature: particles spread faster

The higher the temperature, the faster the diffusion.

4. How surface area affects the speed of diffusion.

Smaller 3D surface, fewer particles can move across

Bigger 3D surface, more move across in the same time

The bigger the surface area, the faster the diffusion.

5. How concentration gradient affects the speed of diffusion.

When a substance is in two areas, concentration gradient is the difference between the concentrations.

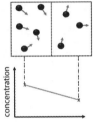

points on the graph are concentrations in each area

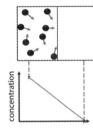

this concentration difference is larger so the concentration gradient is steeper

If you draw a line through the points, concentration gradient is the steepness of the slope.

The steeper the concentration gradient, the faster the diffusion.

 Solve

✓ Claim

✓ Evidence

✓ Reasoning

A and D will have a net movement of oxygen into the cell.
The table shows that in A and D, the concentration of oxygen is higher outside than inside.
Oxygen flows by diffusion - it moves from an area of high to low concentration.
The diagrams show the direction of diffusion. Oxygen will only move into cells A and D.

✓ Claim

✓ Evidence

✓ Reasoning

Oxygen will diffuse faster into cell D than into cell A.
The table of data shows that D has the larger difference in concentration between outside and inside, 5.4-2.2 = 3.2 mg/l.
The steeper the concentration gradient, the faster the rate of diffusion. D has the steeper concentration gradient, so oxygen will diffuse across the cell membrane in cell D the fastest.

Your turn

1

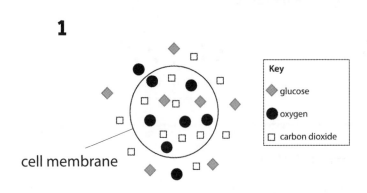

cell membrane

Key
◆ glucose
● oxygen
□ carbon dioxide

Glucose, oxygen and carbon dioxide can diffuse through cell membranes.
The diagram shows the location of molecules at the start of an experiment.
Use the diagram to:
a) Give the direction of movement of each molecule.
b) State which molecule will diffuse the fastest.

2

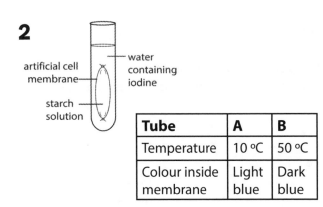

water containing iodine

artificial cell membrane

starch solution

Tube	A	B
Temperature	10 ºC	50 ºC
Colour inside membrane	Light blue	Dark blue

Janice set up two tubes like the one in the diagram. Iodine can cross the artificial cell membrane but starch cannot. The two substances react to produce a blue colour. Janice put the tubes into water baths at different temperatures for 1 minute. She recorded the colour of the water inside the membranes.

Explain the difference in the results.

3

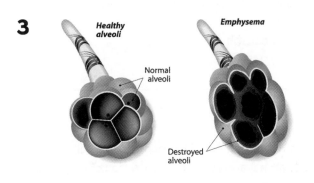

Healthy alveoli

Emphysema

Normal alveoli

Destroyed alveoli

Emphysema is a lung disease which causes the walls of the alveoli to break down. Alveoli are tiny sacs where gases pass between the air and the blood.
Explain how emphysema affects the rate of gas exchange.

4

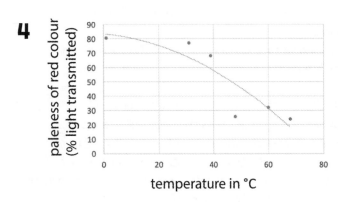

Rose cut six equal cubes of beetroot and put them in beakers of water at different temperatures. She watched the red colour move into the water from the beetroot.
After 5 minutes she measured how pale the red colour was in each beaker, by the percentage of light that passed through.

Explain the pattern shown in the graph.

| **1** | /3 | **2** | /3 | **3** | /3 | **4** | /3 | Total | /12 | © Mastery Science 2018 |

7.5 Explain osmosis changes

Ana tested the effect of salt solution on a parsnip. She dissolved different masses of salt into containers of pure water. Then she added pieces of parsnip into tubes of each salt solution. She weighed the parsnips beforehand, left the pieces in the solution for 2 hours, and then dried and reweighed them.

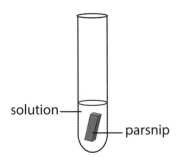

solution

parsnip

Solution	Mass of salt in 1 dm³ water in grams	Mass of parsnip at start in grams	Mass of parsnip at end in grams
A	25	4.62	4.84
B	50	4.54	4.70
C	75	4.60	4.64
D	100	4.59	4.44

Explain the pattern in her results.

Detect

✓ Values
✓ Unknown

✓ Concept

The parsnip piece in solution D lost mass but all the other pieces gained mass. I need to explain why.

The parsnip pieces were in different concentrations of salt solutions and their mass changed. This question must be about osmosis.

Recall

What happens during osmosis?

1. How water moves across a membrane by osmosis.
Diagrams can be used to show what happens during osmosis.

Particles hit the partially permeable membrane.

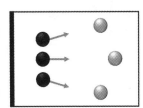

water particle ⚪

solute particle ⚫

Water particles can pass through.

Solute particles do not pass through.

They bounce back and collide with solvent particles, pushing them away.

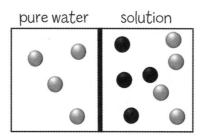

pure water   solution

If water particles are pushed away, there are fewer of them near the membrane.

Overall

When there is a difference in solute concentration, and a partially permeable membrane, there is a net movement of water particles from the less concentrated solution to the more concentrated solution.

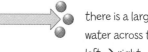 there is a larger movement of water across the membrane left → right

 and a smaller movement of water right → left

 the net movement is left → right

 Solve

✓ **Claim**

In solutions A-C, the parsnip's mass increased. But in D, with the biggest salt concentration, the parsnip's mass decreased. Water must have moved out of cell D by osmosis. That means the solute concentration inside the parsnip was been lower than 100 g/dm³ but higher than 75 g/dm³.

✓ **Evidence**
✓ **Reasoning**

outside cell   inside cell

net water movement

Solutions A-C: low solute concentration.
When the concentration is 25-75 g/dm³ the parsnip's mass increases. This happens because the solute concentration inside the parsnip cell is higher than outside, So, there is a net movement of water into the cell by osmosis. This increases the mass of the parsnip.

✓ **Evidence**
✓ **Reasoning**

How can osmosis change the mass?

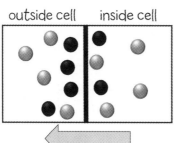

outside cell   inside cell

net water movement

Solution D: high solute concentration.
When the concentration is 100 g/dm³, the parsnip's mass decreases. This happens because the solute concentration inside the parsnip cell is lower than outside, There is a net movement of water out of the cell by osmosis which decreases the mass of the parsnip.

1   Matt investigated the sugar content of a sports drink.

Concentration of sugar solution in mol/dm^3	Change in mass of bag after 20 mins %
0.2	+55
0.4	- 8
0.6	- 22
0.8	- 48

He made four bags from artificial partially permeable membranes. He filled each bag with the drink and put them in different sugar solutions for 20 minutes. He weighed the bags before and after and calculated the percentage change in mass.

Explain the pattern in the results.

2

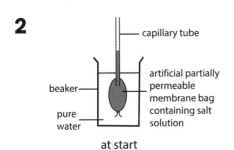

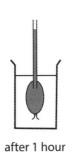

at start   after 1 hour

Malik sets up the equipment as shown.
Use a labelled diagram to explain the result in terms of particle movement.

3

The diagram shows an osmosis investigation. Daisy cuts a potato in half and makes a small well in the centre. She fills it with salt. An hour later, the well is filled with salt solution.

Explain this observation.

4

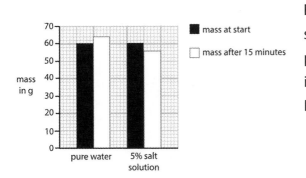

Ed takes two chicken eggs and dissolves their shells. The egg contents are now covered only by a partially permeable membrane. He places each egg in a different liquid for 15 minutes.
Explain the results shown by the bar chart.

1	/3	**2**	/3	**3**	/3	**4**	/3	Total	/12

7.6 Using stem cells

Max has thalassemia. It is caused by a mistake in the genetic material of his stem cells. They do not make healthy red blood cells. Max could be treated with a stem cell transplant. The cells could come from his own body, his brother who is free from the disease, or from a donated embryo.

Explain which source of stem cells would be most effective.

 Detect

✓ **Concept**
✓ **Values**
✓ **Unknown**

This question is about using stem cells to treat a condition.
I know Max's body does not produce healthy red blood cells and that he needs new stem cells to replace the faulty ones.
I need to think about all the possible sources of stem cells, and decide which one has the properties needed to cure the disease.

 Recall

What are the different types of stem cell?

1. How stem cells make specialised cells.

Stem cell are undifferentiated cells

They can divide to produce to many stem cells.

They can differentiate into specialised cells.

2. Where stem cells are found.

In embryos.

In some adult tissues and organs.

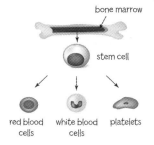

bone marrow

stem cell

red blood cells   white blood cells   platelets

3. How therapeutic cloning can make stem cells.

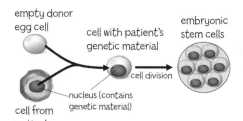

empty donor egg cell

cell with patient's genetic material

embryonic stem cells

cell division

cell from patient

nucleus (contains genetic material)

Therapeutic cloning makes embryonic stem cells containing the patient's genetic material.

Recall

Which type can help Max?

Type	Source	Pro (+) Con (−)
Embryonic stem cells	An embryo Supplies new cells for the embryo as it grows and develops	**+** Can differentiate into any cell in the body **−** The embryo has to be destroyed
Adult stem cells	Some tissues and organs Supplies new cells for growth and to replace damaged cells	**+** Can differentiate into some specialised cell e.g. blood cells **−** Cannot change into all types of specialised cell
Donated stem cells	Adult donor or donated embryo (left over from fertility treatments)	**+** Large source of stem cells **−** Risk of rejection (cells are foreign to patient's body). Lower risk if donor is genetically similar, like parent or sibling
Cloned cells	An embryo formed from the patient's cells using therapeutic cloning	**+** No risk of rejection **−** Has not yet been used in humans The embryo has to be destroyed

 Solve

Max needs healthy stem cells to replace his faulty ones. They must differentiate into red blood cells. There are several sources and here are the pros and cons:

1. His own adult stem cells.
Con (−) These would not work because he has faulty genetic material - his own stem cells would produce unhealthy red blood cells.

2. Donated adult stem cells from his brother.
Pro (+) His brother could donate stem cells from his bone marrow. They can differentiate into blood cells. As his brother is healthy, the blood cells produced will be healthy. As his brother has similar genetic material, the risk of Max's body rejecting foreign cells is small.

3. Donated embryonic stem cells.
Pro (+) They can differentiate to form any specialised cells, including blood cells.
Con (−) The stem cells have different genetic material to Max so there is a high chance they will be rejected by his body.

Overall, the best option for Max is to implant his brother's bone marrow stem cells.

Hint p.122

1

Stem cells can be grown in the lab to make skin tissue and replace the damaged skin of burn patients.

What source of stem cells would be the best choice for this treatment? Give a reason for your answer.

2

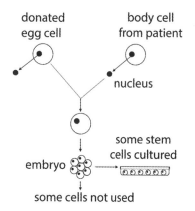

The diagram shows a way of making stem cells.

Explain why embryonic stem cells produced like this might be more useful for medical treatments than stem cells from a donated embryo.

3

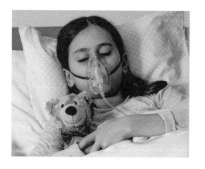

Laura has cystic fibrosis. Cells in her lungs and intestines produce a sticky mucus. This is because a mistake in her genetic material causes the cell membranes to stop working.
In the future scientists hope to use therapeutic cloning to cure diseases.
Explain whether therapeutic cloning could be used to treat Laura's cystic fibrosis.

4

In 2007, researchers discovered how to reprogramme skin stem cells to behave like embryonic stem cells. They did this by changing the genetic material in the cells.
Explain the advantages of this technique for stem cell therapies over other sources of stem cells.

1 /3 **2** /3 **3** /3 **4** /3 Total /12 © Mastery Science 2018

8.1 Gene function

```
GAA AAC TCT TTA TTG
```
lactase gene

```
GAA AAC TCT CTA TTG
```
Sandra's DNA

Sandra feels ill when she drinks milk. Her body does not produce lactase. Lactase is protein that breaks down lactose, a sugar in milk.

The diagram shows the DNA for part of the lactose gene, and the same part in Sandra's DNA.

Explain why Sandra cannot break down lactose.

 Detect

✓ **Diagram**
✓ **Values**

```
GAA AAC TCT TTA TTG

GAA AAC TCT CTA TTG
```

There is a difference in the letters in the two strands.

✓ **Unknown**
✓ **Concept**

I need to explain how this change results in Sandra not breaking down lactose. This question is about genes and how they relate to proteins.

 Recall

1. How genes are a code, made up of substances called bases.

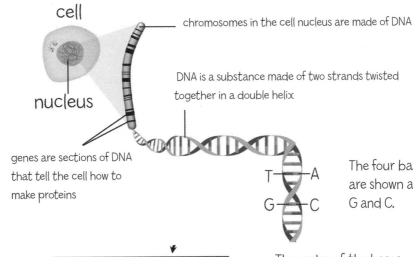

cell

chromosomes in the cell nucleus are made of DNA

nucleus

DNA is a substance made of two strands twisted together in a double helix

genes are sections of DNA that tell the cell how to make proteins

T——A
G——C

The four bases in DNA are shown as letters A, T, G and C.

```
GAA AAC TCT TTA TTG
```

The order of the bases forms the code.

Sometimes there is a mistake (mutation). One base is added, deleted or substituted for another.

2. How bases code for amino acids.

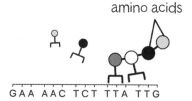

amino acids

GAA AAC TCT TTA TTG

Each group of 3 bases is a code for one amino acid.

Amino acids are brought to the ribosomes in the cell, and join to form a chain.

3. How chains of amino acids make proteins.

Proteins are the molecules that carry out many cell functions. They are made up of chains of amino acids.

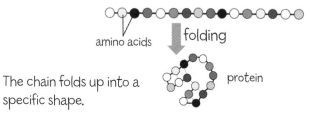

amino acids

folding

The chain folds up into a specific shape.

protein

The order of the amino acids decides the shape the chain folds into. The protein needs to be the right shape to do its job.

 Solve

✓ Claim

✓ Evidence

✓ Reasoning

Sandra's DNA has a mutation.
There is a difference in the letters for her gene and the gene for lactase. The base T has been substituted for the base C.
This is a mistake in her DNA, called a mutation.

✓ Claim

✓ Evidence

✓ Reasoning

The protein produced by Sandra's DNA will not do its job of breaking down lactose.
The gene for lactase contains the three bases TTA. Sandra's gene contains CTA.
Each group of three bases is a code for an amino acid.
In Sandra's cells the wrong amino acid will be used in the chain so the order of the amino acids is wrong. The chain will not fold up in the correct way.
The protein made will not have the correct shape so will not be able to do its job, of breaking down lactose, correctly.

1

X   Y

Cystic fibrosis is a disease where the body makes sticky mucus.

It is caused by a protein in the cell membrane, called CFTR, which does not work properly.

X shows part of the CFTR gene in a person without cystic fibrosis. Y shows the same part of the gene of a patient with the disease.

Explain why the patient has cystic fibrosis.

2

Melanin produces colour in animal fur.

Tyrosinase is a protein needed to make melanin.

Explain why this deer has white fur.

3

DNA bases	Amino acid
AAT	N
AAC	N
AAA	K
AAG	K
AGT	S
AGC	S
AGA	R
AGG	R

Strand A   X   Y

T T T
G G G
A A A

A A A
G G G
C T C

T T T
A A A
A A A

A A A
A A A
T T A

There are 20 different amino acids. The table shows how DNA bases code for some of these amino acids. Strand A is normal DNA. Strands X and Y show strands with mutations.

Explain why only the mutation in strand Y affects cell activity.

4

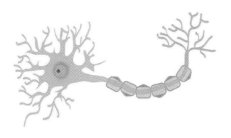

Huntington's disease is a inherited disorder that affects the nervous system. Sufferers cannot make a vital protein for healthy nerve cells.

Now scientists are able to edit genes by changing the order of the DNA bases.

Explain how this could help cure Huntington's disease.

Example

8.2 Construct Punnett Squares

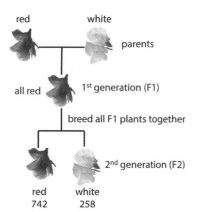

red   white

parents

all red   1st generation (F1)

breed all F1 plants together

2nd generation (F2)

red   white
742   258

In pea plants, the red flower allele is dominant and the white flower allele recessive. A scientist bred pea plants over two generations. He counted the numbers of red and white flower plants in the 2nd generation (F2).

Draw a genetic diagram to explain the ratio of red : white flowers seen in F2.

Detect

- ✓ **Concept**
- ✓ **Values**
- ✓ **Diagram**
- ✓ **Unknown**

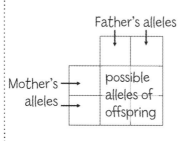

Father's alleles

Mother's alleles

possible alleles of offspring

This question is about inheritance of one gene (monohybrid inheritance) and showing this in a genetic diagram.

The question shows that flower colour is inherited and gives the ratio of red : white flowers in F2.

I need to work out which alleles the F1 plants have. Then use a Punnett square to show the possible combinations of alleles in F2.

Recall

1. How a gene has different forms called alleles.

chromosome

red allele

white allele

This is the red flower allele, written **A** (upper case = dominant)

This is the white flower allelee, written **a** (lower case = recessive)

2. How an organism inherits one allele from each parent.

There are 3 possible combinations – called the genotype.

Aa   **AA**   **aa**

one of each allele (heterozygous)   two of the same allele (homozygous)

3. How the genotype determines which feature the plant has.

AA   **Aa**   **aa**

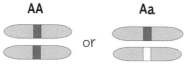

or   →   red

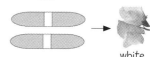

→   white

If there is one dominant allele, it always develops.

The recessive allele only develops if there are two.

Recall

4. How to draw a Punnett square diagram.

A Punnett square shows all the possible combinations of the parents' alleles.

Step 1. Write in the parents' alleles

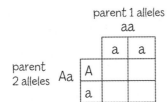

parent 1 alleles
aa

parent 2 alleles Aa

Step 2. Fill in the combinations

each offspring has one of the 4 possible combinations

What would the parent's alleles be in the question?

5. How to interpret a Punnett square diagram.

Two combinations are Aa   red flowers

Two combinations are aa   white flowers.

red : white
= 2 : 2
= 1 : 1

Ratio of red : white flowers
2 combinations make red flowers, and 2 make white so the number of red and white flowers should be about the same.

red flowers / total
= 2/4
= 1/2

Proportion of plants with each colour
2 out of 4 combinations make red flowers which is simplified to 1 in 2. So you can expect that 1 in 2 of the offspring will have red flowers.

50% chance of red
50% chance of white

Probability of each colour
The fraction 1 in 2 means the probability of any offspring having red flowers is 50%.

Solve

✓ **Claim**

Aa

	A	a
A	AA	Aa
a	Aa	aa

Aa

Punnett square diagram. It shows how two Aa parents breed to produce the 3:1 ratio observed in the F2 generation.

✓ **Evidence**
✓ **Reasoning**

3:1 ratio. First I can calculate the ratio of red : white flower plants in the F2 generation.
red : white
742 : 258
ratio = 724/258 = 2.8
There are approximately 3 red flower plants for every 1 white.

✓ **Evidence**
✓ **Reasoning**

F1 generation. The genotypes cannot be AA because two dominant alleles don't produce any white flowers. They can't be aa because some offspring have red flowers. So the F1 plants must be both Aa.

From Punnett square I can deduce that:
3 combinations make red flowers: AA, Aa, Aa.
1 combination makes white flowers: aa.

Your turn

1

wrinkled seed   round seed

The seeds of pea plants have two alleles for shape: round (R) and wrinkled (r). A scientist bred two kinds of peas together:

- round-seed plants
- wrinkled-seed plants

The offspring were all round-seeded. He bred some of the offspring together and produced 4935 round-seed and 1645 wrinkled-seed plants. Use a Punnett square to explain these results.

2

In mice there are two alleles for fur colour: grey and white. Two grey mice were bred to produce 52 offspring. 25 of the offspring were white and 27 were grey.

Use a Punnett square to show the genotypes of the parents and the offspring.

3

In sheep, eye colour is determined by a single gene. The allele for brown eyes is dominant (E) and the blue eyes allele recessive (e).
A male sheep that is heterozygous for eye colour is mated over many years with a female sheep with blue eyes. They have 12 offspring.

What is the most likely ratio of brown to blue eyes in the lambs?

4

Polydactyly is an inherited condition that produces an extra finger. It is caused by a dominant allele. A woman who has polydactyly has two children with a man who does not. One child inherits polydactyly but not the other.

Calculate the probability that a third child will have polydactyly.

| **1** | /3 | **2** | /3 | **3** | /3 | **4** | /3 | Total | /12 |

Example

8.3 Family tree evidence

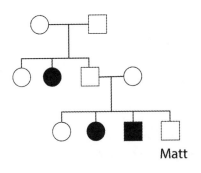

○ female without PKU

● female with PKU

☐ male without PKU

■ male with PKU

Matt's family suffer from PKU. It is a recessive disorder that affects the brain. The family tree shows the pattern of inheritance.

What is the probability that Matt is a carrier of PKU?

🔍 **Detect**

This question is about interpreting family tree diagrams.

PKU is an inherited disorder. The white square tells us that Matt is a male without PKU, but he could be a carrier.

To work out the probability that Matt is a carrier, I need to first work out the geno-type of his parents.

⊘ **Concept**

⊘ **Values**

⊘ **Unknown**

⚙️ **Recall**

1. How a family tree shows genetic history.

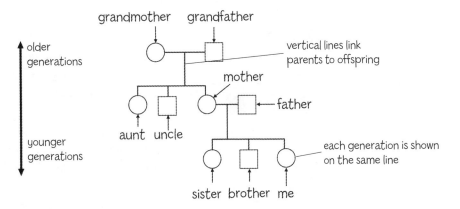

2. How to represent genotypes.

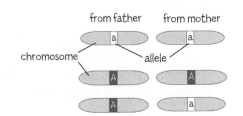

chromosome   allele

A person inherits either:
- One recessive allele from each parent (aa)
- Two dominant alleles (AA)
- One recessive allele and one dominant (Aa)

3. How to work out genotypes from a family tree.

Inherited disorders can be recessive or dominant.

Recessive disorder: A sufferer has two recessive alleles (aa).

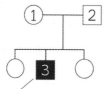

must be aa - two copies of the recessive allele

I can work out what the genotypes of 1 and 2 are by looking at the genotypes of their children.

I know 3 inherited aa. An allele came from each parent 1 and 2.

So I can work out that 1 and 2 must both be Aa. They do not have the disorder but are carriers of the recessive allele.

Dominant disorder: A sufferer has a copy of the dominant allele (Aa or AA).

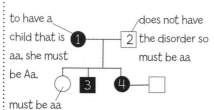

to have a child that is aa, she must be Aa.

does not have the disorder so must be aa

must be aa

I can work out the genotypes of 3 and 4. They have the disorder so they have at least one dominant A gene. They must have got it from their mother (1). That means 3 and 4 must both be Aa.

4. How a Punnett square shows the proportion of offspring genotypes.

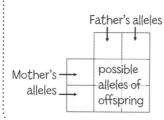

Father's alleles

Mother's alleles

possible alleles of offspring

A Punnett square shows all the possible combinations of the parents' alleles.

Why must 3 be aa?

Why can't 1 be AA?

 Solve

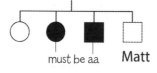

must be aa   Matt

I need to find out the genotypes of Matt's parents. Then I can use a Punnett square to work out the probability of him being a carrier (Aa).

PKU is a recessive disorder. I know Matt's brother and sister both have PKU, so they must be aa. They inherited a copy of the recessive allele from both parents.

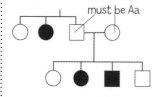

must be Aa

I know the parents do not have PKU - so they are either AA or Aa. But they have children with PKU so they must both be carriers, Aa.

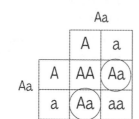

Aa

	A	a
A	AA	Aa
a	Aa	aa

Aa

A Punnett square shows the proportion of carriers (Aa) in the offspring is 2 in 4, or 1 in 2.
That means the probability of a child being a carrier is 50%. Therefore the probability that Matt is a carrier is 50%.

1

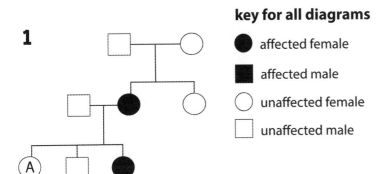

key for all diagrams

- ● affected female
- ■ affected male
- ○ unaffected female
- □ unaffected male

Sickle cell disease is a recessive disorder. The diagram shows the pattern of sickle cell disease in a family.

What is the probability that female A is carrier of sickle cell disease?

2

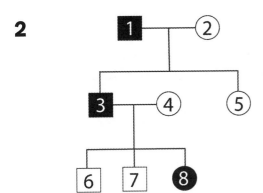

The family tree shows the inheritance of Stickler syndrome. It is caused by a dominant allele.

What is the genotype of person 8? Explain how you worked it out.

3

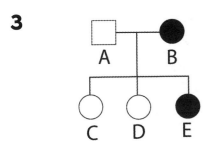

Cystic fibrosis is caused by a faulty protein in the membrane of some cells. It is a recessive genetic disorder and the diagram shows its inheritance.

a) Give the genotypes of people A and B.
Use the symbols:
n = recessive allele
N = dominant allele.
b) Explain how you worked out your answer.

4

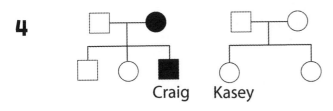

Craig   Kasey

Marfan syndrome is caused by a dominant allele. Kasey and Craig plan to have children.

What is the probability that their child will inherit Marfan syndrome?

Student Workbook
not to be
photocopied

| **1** | /3 | **2** | /3 | **3** | /3 | **4** | /3 | Total | /12 |

9.1 Population distribution

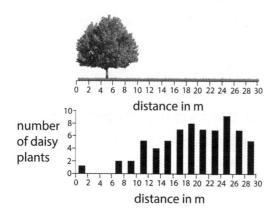

number of daisy plants

distance in m

A class studied how daisy plants were distributed across part of their school field. They recorded the number of plants in 1 m x 1 m quadrats, at 2 m intervals along a transect. The chart shows the data.

Explain why the daisies are not evenly distributed.

Detect

✓ Values

✓ Unknown
✓ Concept

The diagram shows a tree at 5 m and its leaves extending from 0 to 10 m. The chart shows the number of daisies from 0-10 m are low, but get higher from 10-30 m.
I need to explain the reason for this pattern.
This question is about what affects the distribution of organisms.

Recall

1. How individuals in a habitat are distributed.
Distribution means how individual organisms in a species are spread across an area.

What does the bar chart show about the spread of daisies?

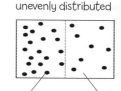

evenly distributed

unevenly distributed

same population

population high   population low

1. How to measure distribution.
This is done by sampling, which is counting the number of organisms in small areas.

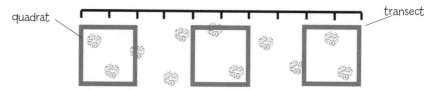

quadrat

transect

1. Make a line along the field (transect).
2. Place square frames (quadrats) at regular intervals.
3. Count the number of organisms in each quadrat.

The sample estimates how the population changes across the whole field.

3. How conditions affect distribution.

The conditions (factors) in an area affect whether organisms can survive.
Factors can be abiotic (non-living) or biotic (living). Some that affect plants are:

Abiotic factors	Biotic factors
• light intensity • temperature ⎤ • carbon dioxide level ⎥ for growth • moisture level ⎥ • mineral level ⎦ • wind intensity & direction • pH	• animals that eat plants • pathogens • competition with other plants for resources

If abiotic factors vary in an area, it affects distribution.

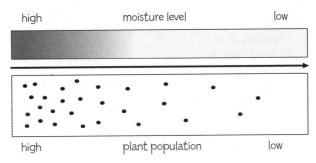

As the factor is needed for growth, the more there is, the bigger the plant population.

 Solve

✓ Claim	The daisy plants show uneven distribution, and this is partly caused by an abiotic factor, the shade from the tree.
✓ Evidence	The number of daisies found between 0 - 10 m was low. The number found between 10 and 30 m was higher.
✓ Reasoning	The tree creates shade and so reduces the light intensity. Between 10 - 30 m there is no shade – high light intensity. Plants need light for growth. So between 0 - 10 m their population is low. It increases with the higher light intensity between 10 - 30 m.
✓ Claim	The uneven distribution could also be caused by a biotic factor, competition.
✓ Evidence	The tree is growing at 5 m. It needs water and minerals from the soil for growth.
✓ Reasoning	Between 0 - 10 m the daisy plants are competing with the tree for water and minerals. This reduces their growth. The competition reduces as daisies get further from the tree because the tree roots only extend a certain distance.

Your turn

1

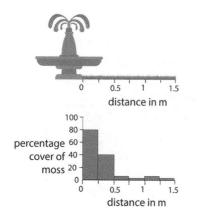

distance in m

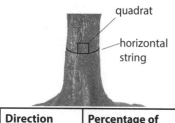

Moss grows best in high moisture levels. Lorelai investigated its distribution across her garden. She used a quadrat to record the percentage of a 0.25 m x 0.25 m area covered with moss.
The diagram shows a side view of the area.

Explain the distribution of moss she found.

2

quadrat

horizontal string

Direction quadrat is facing	Percentage of area covered in algae
North	72%
East	44%
South	2%
West	21%

Algae grows best in moist environments. A class studied the distribution of algae on a tree trunk. The diagram shows how they carried out the investigation.
They measured the percentage cover of algae with the quadrat facing north, south, east and west.
The table shows their results.
Explain a possible reason for the distribution of algae

3

Plant species	Number of plants in each quadrat							
	1	2	3	4	5	6	7	8
Sundew	0	0	0	0	0	0	17	15
Rush	0	0	10	8	9	0	0	0
Bracken	2	4	1	0	0	0	0	0
Factors								
Soil moisture content (%)	15	15	30	35	38	50	60	80
pH	5.6	5.6	5.8	6.0	6.0	6.0	5.8	5.7

The distribution of plants along a section of heathland was investigated by placing quadrats at intervals along a transect.
Some measurements of factors were also taken.
The results are shown in the table.
Suggest a reason for the distribution of each species.

4

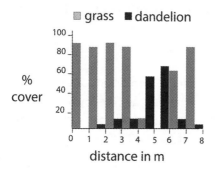

distance in m

Grass only survives in high light intensity. Dandelions survive in low and high light intensity.
Bethany's garden has 2 m diameter trampoline. She measured the percentage cover of both plants using quadrats at 1 m intervals along a transect.

a) Predict where the trampoline is, with a reason.
b) Explain the distribution of both plant species.

9.2 Impacts on biodiversity

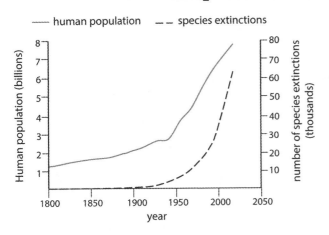

— human population   -- species extinctions

Scientists are concerned about Earth losing its biodiversity. The solid line on the graph shows how the human population changed over the last two centuries.

Suggest why the number of species extinctions has followed a similar pattern.

 Detect

- ✓ **Values**
- ✓ **Unknown**
- ✓ **Concept**

The graph shows both the human population and number of extinctions rose fastest in the last 100 years.
It's possible that one caused the other. I need to work out how.
This question is about biodiversity and how humans have an impact on it.

Recall

1. Biodiversity means the variety of organisms.

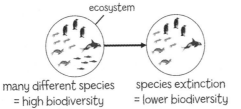

ecosystem

many different species = high biodiversity

species extinction = lower biodiversity

Extinction (when all organisms of a species die), reduces biodiversity. If an ecosystem has many different species, resources are available for other populations, like humans.

2. Why humans need resources and create waste.

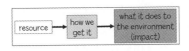

resource → how we get it → what it does to the environment (impact)

We extract and process raw materials to supply resources. This can destroy habitats and cause pollution. So can getting rid of the waste.

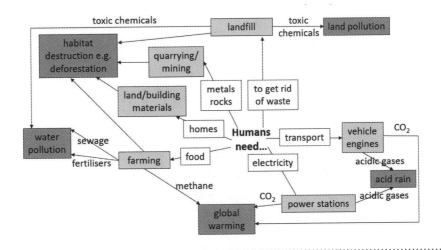

3. How environmental impacts can harm organisms.

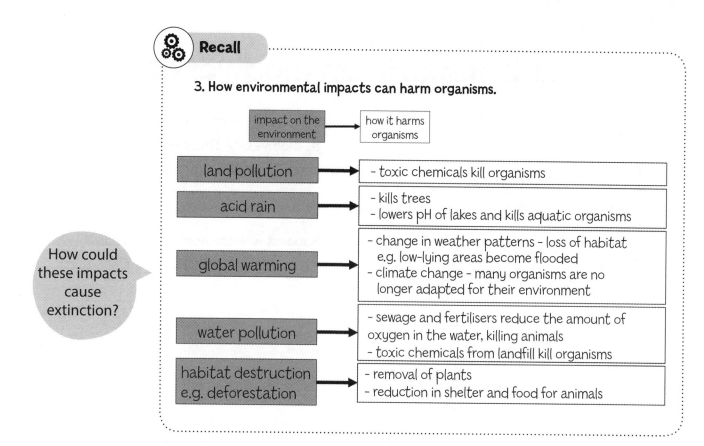

How could these impacts cause extinction?

| impact on the environment | → | how it harms organisms |

land pollution → - toxic chemicals kill organisms

acid rain → - kills trees
- lowers pH of lakes and kills aquatic organisms

global warming → - change in weather patterns - loss of habitat e.g. low-lying areas become flooded
- climate change - many organisms are no longer adapted for their environment

water pollution → - sewage and fertilisers reduce the amount of oxygen in the water, killing animals
- toxic chemicals from landfill kill organisms

habitat destruction e.g. deforestation → - removal of plants
- reduction in shelter and food for animals

 Solve

✓ **Claim**

The combination of more people and higher living standards in the last 100 years has increased the impacts on the environment. This has caused a similar rise in the number of species extinctions.

✓ **Evidence**

The graph shows that after 1900 the human population increased dramatically. The number of species extinctions did too. Species go extinct when all the organisms of that species are killed. This is likely to be because of increasing human activities and their impacts on the environment.

✓ **Reasoning**

Humans need food, electricity, transport, homes, metals and rocks. Obtaining these, and getting rid of waste, impacts on the environment.
These human activities produce five main impacts on the environment:

How do human impacts cause extinction?

- land pollution
- acid rain
- global warming
- water pollution
- habitat destruction

Each has a negative effect on organisms and contributes to species extinction. Therefore the increasing numbers of people, who are using more resources, can explain the dramatic rise in species extinctions.

Hint p.122

1

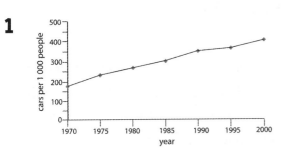

This graph shows data about the use of cars in the UK.

What effects could the trend have had on biodiversity? Explain your answer.

2

Tigers are predators that hunt in the forests of India. Humans use the forests to collect firewood and to provide land for farming.

a) Draw a flowchart to explain why the increasing human population has reduced the tiger population.

b) Explain how the loss of tigers affects the biodiversity of the forests.

3

Scientists counted the number of organisms in water samples from two rivers.

Which river is less polluted? Explain your choice.

4

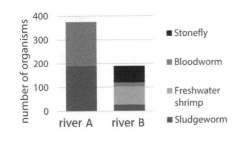

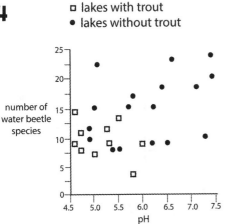

Scientists wanted to find out the effect of human activity on the biodiversity of water beetles.

The graph shows how the number of species depends on the pH and whether trout have been put into the lakes for fishing.

a) Use the graph to explain two ways that human activity can affect the biodiversity of water beetles.

b) Explain which activity has the bigger impact.

Example

9.3 Control disease

The disease Chalara ash dieback makes ash trees lose their leaves and then die. It is caused by fungi. When dead leaves fall from the tree, the fungi reproduce and release spores the following spring.

Explain how the spread of Chalara ash dieback could be prevented.

 Detect

☑ Concept

☑ Values

☑ Unknown

This question is about communicable diseases and how their spread can be prevented.

I know that the spores from fungi infect trees, so Chalara ash dieback is a communicable disease.

First, I need to work out how the disease spreads. Then I need to identify how it can be stopped from spreading.

 Recall

1. How disease organisms move from infected to healthy organisms.

Communicable diseases are infectious - they spread between organisms (animals, plants and single-celled organisms). There are five main ways diseases spread:

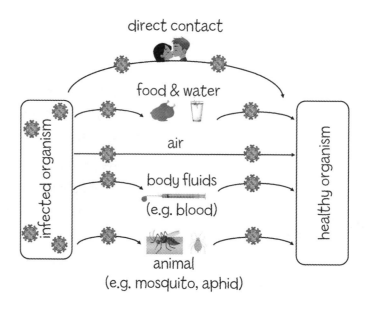

2. How pathogens spread infectious diseases.

Pathogens are microorganisms that cause disease. They grow, reproduce and spread inside, or on, an organism.

 Bacteria enter an organism and reproduce rapidly. They produce poisons (toxins) that damage tissues. e.g. salmonella food poisoning is spread by eating infected food, and gonorrhoea by direct contact during sex.

 Viruses enter an organism's cells and reproduce. New virus particles break out of cells, damaging them. e.g. measles spreads by inhaling droplets from sneezes, and HIV by sex or exchanging body fluids like blood.

 Protists are often carried by animal vectors. e.g. the malarial protist is spread by mosquitoes.

 Fungi reproduce in or on an organism. They can be single-celled, spreading via direct contact or by contaminated food and water. Or they can be multicellular, reproducing by tiny, light spores which enter new organisms. e.g. rose black spot fungi spores are carried in water or air.

 Solve

Claim

Evidence

Reasoning

The spread of Chalara ash dieback could be prevented in two ways: stop dead leaves falling and remove dead leaves from the ground.

I know the disease is caused by fungi. Fungi produce spores that can be carried in water and air. The dead leaves falling in autumn contain the fungi pathogen. They release spores, which travel in the air to infect new leaves in spring. I can summarise information about the fungi in a lifecycle diagram:

Evidence

Reasoning

From the diagram, I can deduce two options for preventing the spread:
1. Stop dead leaves falling
Cutting down and removing infected trees during the summer will stop the infected leaves and twigs falling to the ground.
2. Remove dead leaves
Burning the infected leaves and twigs on the ground during winter will stop the fungi growing and releasing spores into the air.

1

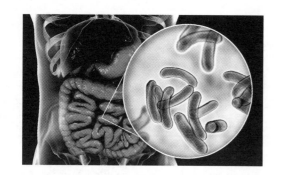

Cholera kills 95,000 people each year around the world. The bacteria infect the intestines, where they cause severe diarrhoea. Bacteria leave the body in the faeces.

Explain how the spread of cholera can be prevented.

2

Ticks are vectors for the bacteria that cause Lyme disease. Imagine that a man from the UK catches Lyme disease when on holiday.

Do you think he should be quarantined (kept away from other people) when he returns, to stop the disease spreading? Give a reason.

3

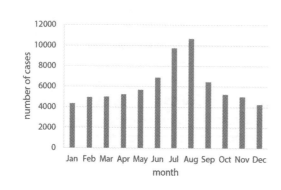

The chart shows the number of cases of salmonella in the EU during 2012.

a) In which months are the numbers of cases highest? Suggest why this is.

b) Explain how the numbers could be reduced.

4

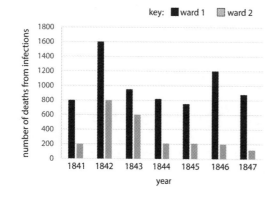

The chart shows the number of women dying from post-birth infections in a 19th century hospital. On Ward 1, babies were delivered mainly by doctors who worked on many other wards. On Ward 2, babies were delivered by midwives who did not work on other wards.

a) Explain a possible cause of the difference in death rates on wards 1 and 2.

b) Suggest how this could have been prevented.

1 /3   **2** /3   **3** /3   **4** /3   Total   /12

Hints

Acceleration

1.1 Distance travelled
Q1. Draw a speed time graph and find the area
Q2. Convert speed and time into m/s and seconds.
Q3. NB. Initial/final speeds are not 0. The area is a trapezium.
Q4. Find the time: time = distance ÷ average speed.

1.2 Acceleration & gradients
Q1. Convert distances to metres and time to seconds.
Q2. Which information do you need to find acceleration?
Q3. Which shows velocity decreasing upwards and increasing downwards?
Q4. Use v - u = a x t (u=0). For C-D, use v from a) as u.

1.3 Equation of motion
Q1. The initial speed is zero.
Q2. Rearrange the equation to make 'a' the subject.
Q3. Calculate acceleration at each speed. Use correct units.
Q4. For b) use the value for speed from a) as u.

1.4 Newton's 1st law
Q1. Final velocity is lower than that before parachute opens.
Q2. Horizontal forces: engine thrust, tension in toe bar and drag. Are these forces balanced?
Q3. Horizontal forces: engine thrust and drag. Vertically: weight and upthrust.
Q4. Horizontal forces: thrust, and wind. Vertically: weight and upthrust.

1.5 Adding vectors
Q1. Combine parallel forces into one before drawing.
Q2. Use a large scale e.g. 1 cm:10 N.
Q3. Do you add or subtract the forces to combine them?
Q4. Measure to the nearest 0.1 cm (arrows) and 1° (angles).

1.6 Vector components
Q1. The girl is balanced so the vertical components of the tension acting up equal weight acting down.
Q2. How does horizontal component of pull change when angle decreases?
Q3. Vector diagrams can be used to adds speeds. Vertical component is speed and direction of river current.
Q4. To find upthrust, measure the resultant (the hypotenuse).

Heating

2.1 Particle energy transfer
Q1. For each layer, what property affects the energy transfer?
Q2. How do structure and thickness affect the energy transfer? What heat loss is needed in warm/cold water?
Q3. How do surfaces and thicknesses affect rate of energy transfer at midday?
Q4. Consider surface coating, structure and thickness.

2.2 Thermal transfer rates
Q1. a) Which cup has the higher rate of energy transfer? b) What will the final temperature of the coffee be?
Q2. Can fluffy layer offer any insulation when on the outside?
Q3. Which factor that affects energy transfer matters here?
Q4. How do the thickness and thermal conductivity of the heat sink material help?

2.3 Specific heat capacity
Q1. Use the efficiency as a decimal to find output energy. Use this to calculate specific heat capacity.
Q2. Use the equation with mass in kg.
Q3. Use the equation to find temperature difference, and add the initial temperature.
Q4. When the temperature decreases E and Δθ are negative.

2.4 Latent heat
Q1. a) Scale up the energy needed for 1 g. b) What is the energy transfer when the sauce sets?
Q2. a) Scale up the energy needed for 0.25 kg. b) Look at which graph has the longer flat part.
Q3. a) Scale down the energy needed for 1 kg. b) What are the state changes for i), ii) and iii)?
Q4. a) Use the equation. b) Notice the energy is for 5 seconds.

2.5 Gas pressure
Q1. There are tiny holes in the balloon skin.
Q2. How do particle move at higher temperatures?
Q3. The walls collapse if the outside pressure is much bigger than inside pressure.
Q4. When friction slows the car, where does the K.E. go?

2.6 Liquid pressures
Q1. The water from the taps should be at high pressure.
Q2. The pressure inside is atmospheric pressure at sea level.
Q3. How can the diver ensure the pressure changes slowly?
Q4. Would water at high or low pressure flow more quickly?

Sound & waves

3.1 Sound waves
Q1. The wave travels along the tube. Does Alan's hand moving the tube back and forth or at right angles?
Q2. The waves travel along the bridge. Is the vibration in that direction or at right angles?
Q3. Link high/low pressure in the wave to movement of the diaphragm and peaks/troughs on the oscilloscope.
Q4. Think about which directions the particles vibrate to cause surface ripples and underwater sound.

3.2 Wave properties
Q1. When does ball return to start position after vibration?
Q2. a) What happens to air pressure when amplitude increases? b) Recall that frequency is 1/period.
Q3. Find frequency of each motor and decide whether it is in the frequency range of reef sound.
Q4. How many wavelengths are made in the time shown? What is the time for one wavelength?

3.3 Wave speed equation
Q1. a) Find wave speed first. b) Speed changes in a new material, but what property stays the same?
Q2. a) Use the wave equation. b) What properties change or stay the same in a new material?
Q3. a) How does the pitch relate to frequency? b) Use the speed from part a).
Q4. Use the wave equation with the material where you have two values. What stays the same in a new material?

Periodic table

4.1 Represent subatomic particles
Q1. A helium nucleus contains 2 neutrons and 2 protons.
Q2. Why do atoms have no overall charge?
Q3. Find the atomic numbers of neon and argon – how are the atoms different?
Q4. How can you increase the mass number of hydrogen?

4.2 Calculate relative atomic mass
Q1. Which isotope has the highest percentage?
Q2. The ratio 1 : 3 converted into a percentage is 25% : 75%.
Q3. A_r is the average of the isotopes so what must their relative abundances be?
Q4. The abundances is a fraction. Convert into a percentage.

4.3 Periodic patterns
Q1. It does not conduct electricity, so must be a non-metal.
Q2. What happens to the number of shells down a group?
Q3. Use the data to work out if it is a solid, liquid or gas.
Q4. What are hydrogen's properties and its outer electrons?

4.4 Reactions of groups 1 & 7
Q1. Use the equations to work out the name of the products.
Q2. Consider where each element is placed in its group.
Q3. Group 1 elements react with moisture in the air.

Hints

Q4. Solution C and halogen D are made by displacement.

Matter & energy

5.1 Products of combustion
Q1. What type of combustion does a yellow flame indicate?
Q2. What is formed when hydrogen is oxidised?
Q3. It is not just carbon that is oxidised during combustion.
Q4. How many water (H_2O) molecules must there be on the right to balance equation?

5.2 Calculate bond energies
Q1. Negative energy means the reaction is exothermic.
Q2. Multiply the number of bonds in each substance by the number outside the bracket (where there is one).
Q3. Find the overall energy change from Emma's numbers.
Q4. If energy released when bonds are made is higher than the energy to break bonds, the reaction is endothermic.

5.3 Balance symbol equations
Q1. The word equation is: hydrogen + nitrogen $\rightarrow$ ammonia.
Q2. Do not count individual O, S and H atoms, treat them as groups OH and SO_4.
Q3. How many Fe and O atoms will balance the equation?
Q4. Write the equation - what is the ratio of $H_2 : O_2$?

5.4 Calculate mass in equations
Q1. 32 g (16 x 2) of oxygen is needed to completely react with 12 g of carbon. Scale this down.
Q2. Work out the formula mass of iron oxide and iron.
Q3. You do not need the equation to answer this question.
Q4. 56 g of Fe reacts with 32 g of S.

Using resources

6.1 Reactivity series
Q1. The steeper the line, the faster the metal reacts.
Q2. The liquid must be either water or acid.
Q3. Use the reactivity series to compare reactivities.
Q4. More reactive metals form positive ions more easily.

6.2 Predict displacement reactions
Q1. Copper is an unreactive metal.
Q2. The brown colour is copper.
Q3. Hydrogen is displaced from the acid during the reaction.
Q4. Carbon displaces some elements from their compounds.

6.3 Potable water
Q1. Sea water is salty - it is high in sodium chloride.
Q2. What is the name of the process shown in the graph?
Q3. Which process is expensive?
Q4. To see the dissolved substances water must be removed.

6.4 Environmental impact
Q1. What stages of the life cycle does the data show?
Q2. Consider extraction of materials, transport and disposal.
Q3. He could bin it (landfill) or trade it in (reused or recycled)
Q4. Why might the manufacturer not supply information?

Growth & differentiation

7.1 Cell magnification
Q1. To calculate the diameter of the virus use 55 ÷ 450 000.
Q2. Before calculating magnification, make units the same.
Q3. When you x 10 you increase order of magnitude by one.
Q4. The scale line gives you the diameter of cell and nucleus.

7.2 Cell cycle changes
Q1. The cytoplasm volume is the same in parent and daughter cells.
Q2. Chromosomes are copied and the copies are split apart.
Q3. If a stage is fast, will there be many cells at any one time?
Q4. What does the graph show about the amount of DNA?

7.3 Types of cell transport
Q1. Which minerals diffuse and which use active transport.
Q2. Urea only diffuses if there is a concentration difference.

Q3. Cells use oxygen in respiration.
Q4. When respiration stops, glucose is still absorbed. The cell must absorb glucose without using energy.

7.4 Predict diffusion
Q1. Count the molecules on either side of the membrane.
Q2. Which substance diffuses? How does temperature affect the rate?
Q3. How does alveoli breaking down affect diffusion?
Q4. The red colour diffuses out of the beetroot into the water.

7.5 Explain osmosis
Q1. For each concentration, work out if water entered or left.
Q2. First work out where solute concentration is the highest. Then decide which direction water particles move in.
Q3. The salt concentration is higher in the pile than in the cells.
Q4. If the mass goes up, water has gone into the egg; if it goes down, water has moved out of the egg.

7.6 Use stem cells
Q1. Adult stem cells can differentiate into skin cells.
Q2. The embryo has the same genetic material as the patient.
Q3. All Laura's cells have the mistake in the genetic material.
Q4. What are the advantages over other stem cells?

Genetics

8.1 Gene function
Q1. Compare the strands - what is different?
Q2. The deer cannot make melanin – what could cause this?
Q3. Work out the sequence of amino acids coded by strand A and then strands X and Y.
Q4. Inherited diseases are caused by mutations in genes.

8.2 Construct Punnett squares
Q1. 4935 ÷ 1645 = 3. The ratio of wrinkled-seed plants to round-seed plants is 1:3.
Q2. If the parents are both grey but some babies have white fur, which allele must be dominant?
Q3. First work out the genotypes of the parents. Remember, heterozygous genotypes have one of each allele.
Q4. If a child is without polydactyly, what is the man's genotype?

8.3 Family tree evidence
Q1. Their mother has cystic fibrosis - what must her genotype be?
Q2. In a dominant disorder, a sufferer has a copy of the dominant allele (Aa or AA)
Q3. In a recessive disorder a sufferer has two recessive alleles (nn).
Q4. Work out Craig and Kasey's genotypes and use a Punnett square.

Human interaction

9.1 Explain population distribution
Q1. Moss and grass compete for the same resources.
Q2. What abiotic factors decrease the growth of algae?
Q3. Different plants require different levels of abiotic factors.
Q4. Daisies and dandelions compete for the same resources.

9.2 Impacts on biodiversity
Q1. Use the diagram to work out the impacts of cars.
Q2. A flow diagram shows what will happen, with arrows connecting the events. Start with 'more people'.
Q3. How does water pollution affect organisms?
Q4. Both pH and trout affect the number of water beetle species - what is the relationship in each case?

9.3 Control disease
Q1. Faeces enter the water supply, so bacteria infect the water.
Q2. How does Lyme disease pass from the infected person to someone else?
Q3. Salmonella bacteria grow more quickly when it is warm.
Q4. What is the difference in the way doctors/nurses work?

Acknowledgements

GCSE /Y9 Mastery Science Practice Book   First published 2018   ISBN 978-0-9566810-5-8

Text copyright Mastery Science Ltd. Design by Alexandra Okada. Images by Gemma Young.

The publisher would like to thank the following for permission to reproduce photographs:

Images from the Noun Project: p22 Sun: Alvaro Cabrera, p22 Worker carrying box: Gan Khoon Lay
p24 Parker Solar Probe: NASA/Johns Hopkins APL/Ed Whitman
p34 Paddling pool: Frances Rattigan
p42 Wooden Bridge: fumar-porros
p131 Onion cells: Wiki commons

All remaining images copyright free stock from Shutterstock.